VOCABULARY ~~FROM CONTEXT~~ EXT

P9-EET-788

MYSTERIES, CURIOSITIES & WONDERS

Roswell Daily Record

RAAF Captures Flying
On Ranch in Ros...

Claims Army
Is Slacking
Courts Martial

House Passos
Tax Slash by
Large Margin

🏠 Prestwick House

VOCABULARY IN CONTEXT:
MYSTERIES, CURIOSITIES & WONDERS

Senior Editor:

Paul Moliken

Writer:

Stephanie Polukis

Cover and Text Design:

Chris Koniencki

Layout and Production:

Jeremy Clark

Prestwick House

P.O. Box 658 • Clayton, DE 19938
(800) 932-4593 • www.prestwickhouse.com

ISBN: 978-1-62019-352-5
Item: 310623

TABLE OF CONTENTS

THREE SIDES OF THE BERMUDA TRIANGLE

As early as the fifteenth century, people have reported bizarre and terrifying events in the area we refer to as the "Bermuda Triangle." Something about this peculiar location has caused the destruction and disappearance of ships and, in more recent years, airplanes. What is so abnormal about this 500,000 square mile area within a triangle formed by Miami, Puerto Rico, and the island of Bermuda? The **copious** and contradictory theories from many different fields arouse debate among the superstitious, the scientific, and the skeptical.

The term "Bermuda Triangle" wasn't coined until it first appeared in *Argosy* magazine in 1964. But mysterious events had been reported there, even in the time of Christopher Columbus. On his famous voyage in 1492, Columbus and his crew observed odd lights in the sky when they sailed through the area. On September 15th, he recorded in his journal,

> [I]n the early part of the night there fell from heaven into the sea a marvellous [sic] flame of fire....

The fireball in the sky could have been a meteor, but the journal entry on October 11th mentions more unusual activity:

> [The Admiral] at ten o'clock that evening standing on the quarter-deck saw a light, but so small a body that he could not affirm it to be land.... The Admiral again perceived it once or twice, appearing like the light of a wax candle moving up and down...."

What were the strange **anomalies**, the lights that had no explanation? Were they merely the product of people's imaginations? Would they later be **relegated** to the same category as sea monsters and ghost ships? Or was there something unusual flying in the night sky hundreds of years ago?

Within the last century, the Triangle mystery has grown more intense with modern communication fueling the discussion. In 1945, an entire squadron of torpedo bombers, known as "Flight 19," disappeared in the waters southwest of Florida. More suspicious accidents followed. The SS *Marine Sulfur Queen* vanished in a similar fashion in 1963. It was last known to be near the southern tip of the state. In 2017, a small aircraft (a Mitsubishi MU-2B-40) vanished after it left Puerto Rico en route to Florida. Can it be that every one of these circumstances was just bad luck? Millions of people now believe forces at work within the Triangle are beyond the ordinary.

Many theorists **attest** that strange occurrences in the Triangle are the result of alien encounters. Unidentifiable objects in the sky might be visitors from other planets, they say. Some believe that otherworldly technology could interfere with navigational equipment, allowing aliens to abduct entire ships. No scientific evidence can back up these claims, yet they continue to circulate among devoted and enthusiastic UFO **aficionados**.

But maybe the source of the supposedly paranormal events isn't **celestial** at all. What if the **inexplicable** occurrences were caused by mysterious forces *below* the waves?

Myths about Atlantis are almost as popular as those about the Triangle. As it turns out, the two mysteries might, in fact, be connected. For centuries, Atlantis had been considered "lost." Some archaeologists think it may have finally been uncovered. Odd structures—either ruins or natural rock formations—were found near the Bahamas, within the area of the Triangle. Some believers theorize that the **denizens** of Atlantis possessed "energy crystals." These could interfere with navigational devices, leading ships and airplanes off course, ultimately to their doom.

As would be expected, these theories, while exciting, cause scientists to roll their eyes. The disasters might be extraordinary, or they could be entirely natural. In opposition to the imaginative **hypotheses** mentioned earlier, scientists have provided possible reasons of their own.

One scientific explanation deals with clouds that can be incredibly destructive. A few studies suggest large, hexagonal clouds over the ocean cause "microbursts," winds that can create fifty-foot waves. These would certainly be large enough to damage a ship. Combine the waves with 100-mph microburst winds, and you have a recipe for disaster.

Another interesting theory involves methane, the same gas used to generate electricity and heat. In nature, methane becomes trapped in the ocean floor. It does occasionally escape, and as the gas rises in the form of gigantic bubbles, the surface of the water becomes less dense. Hypothetically, the change in density might destroy a ship's ability to float, causing it to sink like a rock to the bottom of the sea. But even if it could cause ships to disappear, what about *planes*? Some researchers believe that the highly combustible gas could ignite, lighting aircraft on fire. Could this information finally solve the mystery?

What if there *were* no mystery of the Bermuda Triangle, though? One explanation sounds more logical than the rest: Statistically, no more disasters happen in the Triangle than anywhere else in the world. People's biased viewpoints of the area may lead them to misinterpret evidence in order to **substantiate** the idea that the Triangle is an especially dangerous place.

Explanations for what happens in the area abound, ranging from paranormal occurrences, to scientific phenomena, to a **cogent** examination of statistics. What *has* caused the wonder and interest associated with the legend of lost ships and planes? Regardless of the answer, the Bermuda Triangle remains a site of mystery. It continues to fascinate those who believe there are still things on Earth that defy our understanding of reality.

EXERCISE 1 / WORD LIST

Use the context in which the word is used to determine what the word probably means. Write a brief definition in the space provided.

1. **aficionado:** _____

   No scientific evidence can back up these claims, yet they continue to circulate among devoted and enthusiastic UFO **aficionados**.

2. **anomaly:** _____

   What were the strange **anomalies**, the lights that had no explanation?

3. **attest:** _____

   Many theorists **attest** that strange occurrences in the Triangle are the result of alien encounters.

4. **celestial:** _____

   But maybe the source of the supposedly paranormal events isn't **celestial** at all. What if the inexplicable occurrences were caused by mysterious forces *below* the waves?

5. **cogent:** _____

   Explanations for what happens in the area abound, ranging from paranormal occurrences, to scientific phenomena, to a **cogent** examination of statistics.

6. **copious:** _____

   The **copious** and contradictory theories from many different fields arouse debate among the superstitious, the scientific, and the skeptical.

7. **denizen:** _____

   Some believers theorize that the **denizens** of Atlantis possessed "energy crystals."

8. **hypothesis:** _____

   In opposition to the imaginative **hypotheses** mentioned earlier, scientists have provided possible reasons of their own.

9. **inexplicable:** _____

But maybe the source of the supposedly paranormal events isn't celestial at all. What if the **inexplicable** occurrences were caused by mysterious forces *below* the waves?

10. **relegate:** _____

Were they merely the product of people's imaginations? Would they later be **relegated** to the same category as sea monsters and ghost ships?

11. **substantiate:** _____

People's biased viewpoints of the area may lead them to misinterpret evidence in order to **substantiate** the idea that the Triangle is an especially dangerous place.

EXERCISE 2 / USING WORDS IN CONTEXT

Fill in the blank with the vocabulary word that best completes the sentence. In some cases, you may need to change the tense or form of a verb or the number of a noun.

hypothesis	anomaly	aficionado	denizen	inexplicable	celestial
copious	cogent	relegate	attest	substantiate	

1. The homeowners _____ that the burglar escaped on foot, rather than in a vehicle.

2. Astrologers believe that studying the movement of planets and other _____ objects can reveal the future.

3. _____ in the earth's magnetic field could explain some of the equipment failure.

4. I can't go to the beach this weekend because of the _____ homework my teacher gave us to do.

5. The mysterious voices in the hallway seemed to _____ Jim's belief that the house was haunted.

6. At family gatherings, my mother always _____ my sister and me to the kids' table.

7. One _____ of Argentina claims that a UFO regularly hovers above her dairy farm.

8. Based on the evidence, Dr. Gilmore's _____ is that a rare virus causes the disease.

4

9. Science-fiction _____ sometimes learn alien languages used in their favorite movies and TV shows.

10. Carly's friends found it _____ that she returned to school to get a degree in biology after being a math teacher for twenty years.

11. The historian presented a(n) _____ argument that Stonehenge had originally been an ancient burial site.

EXERCISE 3 / READING COMPREHENSION AND ANALYSIS

Select the best answers to the following questions based on a close and thorough reading of "Three Sides of the Bermuda Triangle."

1. The "Three Sides" in the title refer to

   A. Miami, Puerto Rico, and the Atlantic Ocean.

   B. the number of times Columbus saw lights in the sky.

   C. Flight 19, the SS *Marine Sulfur Queen*, and the other missing aircraft.

   D. the theories of the superstitious, the scientific, and the skeptical people.

   E. the total number of theories about the Triangle.

2. The quotations from Columbus's journal are included in the passage in order to

   A. arouse interest by mentioning a famous person.

   B. provide a historical account of mysterious incidents in the Triangle.

   C. show that Columbus was an unreliable witness.

   D. argue that the Triangle was invented by imaginative sailors.

   E. retell a story originally published in *Argosy* magazine.

3. What is implied in the statement that stories about the lights in the sky might be put into "the same category as sea monsters and ghost ships"?

   A. Columbus saw sea monsters and ghost ships.

   B. Sea monsters and ghost ships don't exist.

   C. Sea monsters and ghost ships are strange occurrences.

   D. Flying objects are more dangerous than sea monsters and ghost ships.

   E. Nobody believes in sea monsters and ghost ships.

4. Re-read the following excerpt from the passage:

> "Hypothetically, the change in density might destroy a ship's ability to float, causing it to sink like a rock to the bottom of the sea. But even if *it* could cause ships to disappear, what about *planes*?"

The italicized word *it* refers to the

A. sea.

B. bottom.

C. rock.

D. Bermuda Triangle.

E. density.

5. This passage is organized by

A. importance.

B. chronology.

C. topic.

D. source.

E. location.

EXERCISE 4 / MAKING INFERENCES

Choose the best answer.

1. The results of an experiment may be **inexplicable** if they

A. have no practical importance.

B. cannot be repeated.

C. were unpredicted.

D. defy scientific laws.

2. Of the following, which is a correct use of the word **relegate**?

A. Ms. Clark relegated the job of taking attendance to her assistant.

B. Nobody could relegate victory from the football team.

C. Michelle relegated her best jewelry to her daughter.

D. We relegated the homework between the two of us.

3. What might Paul do if he **attests** to be an expert on tropical fish?

   A. deny he is interested in aquatic animals

   B. question whether his ideas are true

   C. identify all the species correctly

   D. go to the aquarium every weekend

4. Which of the following would **substantiate** a theory that aliens exist?

   A. debris from a spaceship

   B. proof that the Loch Ness monster is real

   C. videos revealing that "UFOs" are airplanes

   D. testimonies of unreliable witnesses

5. Based upon its context in the sentence "The term 'Bermuda Triangle' wasn't coined until it first appeared in *Argosy* magazine in 1964," the word *coined* most nearly means

   A. created.

   B. revived.

   C. revised.

   D. understood.

EXERCISE 5 / ROOTS, PREFIXES, AND SUFFIXES

Answer the questions below that are designed to help you arrive at some conclusions about word families and origins.

1. Briefly define **copious** in your own words. What part of speech is **copious**?

   _____

   _____

   A. Consider the following words, which all share the same root:

   • a *unicorn* is a horse-like animal with a single horn growing from its forehead;

   • a three-pointed hat like one worn during the Revolutionary War is called a *tricorne* hat;

   • later in the eighteenth century, a two-peaked or *bicorn* hat (worn with one peak toward the front and one toward the back) became more fashionable.

   What does the root *corn* (Latin *cornu*) most likely mean?

   _____

B. A common item displayed around Thanksgiving in the United States is the *cornucopia*, which is a large horn overflowing with flowers and food, including gourds, grains, and fruit. What is another common term for this item?

_____

How does the word *cornucopia* derive its meaning from its parts?

_____

2. Briefly define **hypothesis** in your own words.

_____

_____

A. Another familiar word that contains a common root with **hypothesis** is *antithesis*. Briefly define *antithesis*. Feel free to consult a dictionary if you need to.

_____

_____

B. What root do these words share?

_____

_____

C. What does the root probably mean?

_____

_____

D. Where else have you most likely encountered this root? What did it mean in that context?

_____

_____

E. What other familiar words probably also use the prefix *hypo–*?

_____

F. Briefly define each of the words you mentioned. Use a dictionary if necessary.

_____

_____

G. What does the prefix *hypo–* most likely mean?

_____

_____

THE MARVEL OF THE MONARCH

Butterfly GPS

If you wanted to travel to a precise location somewhere far away—a small forest in Mexico, for example—how would you get there? You might start with some seriously savvy tech tools. Even a state-of-the-art GPS won't help you navigate the **labyrinthine** forest of intertwining trees once you're there, though. You might stop to ask for directions along the way, but that strategy is unpredictable and can go **awry** quickly. Whatever method you choose, it'll likely involve external tools or resources of some kind. However, what if you decided to trust only your instinctive understanding of how to get there? The monarch butterfly—a primarily North American species adored for its **vibrant** black, orange, and white wings—does exactly that. Unlike us, however, monarchs won't get lost twenty minutes after leaving home.

Every autumn, millions of monarch butterflies migrate across North America in what Lincoln Brower, an expert on monarchs, called "one of the most spectacular natural phenomena in the world." One monarch population makes an especially lengthy journey. These amazing insects travel from the northeastern United States to a forest in the Mexican state of Michoacán, on the country's southwestern coast, up to 3,000 miles away. To achieve this astonishing feat, the butterflies use a genetically encoded ability to rely on two natural guides: the position of the sun in the sky and the earth's magnetic field.

Here Comes the Sun Compass

For centuries, humans have used compasses to guide them to their destinations. Similarly, monarch butterflies use an **innate** sense—what scientists call a "sun compass"—to find their way to one specific forest in Michoacán. They accomplish this feat with a precision that researchers have long sought to comprehend. Monarchs can remain on course by determining whether to fly to the left of, to the right of, or directly toward the sun. This ability, while extraordinary, does have a serious flaw. The sun doesn't remain fixed in the sky, so it's not a stationary reference point. How is it possible for monarchs to overcome this seemingly **insurmountable** obstacle?

Imagine, for a moment, that you're a traveling monarch butterfly. It's morning. It's time to take to the skies and continue the long, difficult journey to Mexico. The sun appears in the east, of course, so in order to head south, you need to fly to the *right* of it. However, the sun is rising by the minute. How can you fly in the correct direction if your critical point of reference moves all the time? It's a good thing you have *circadian rhythm*—an "internal clock" that controls sleep/wake cycles and other **physiological** processes—to tell you how to correctly **orient** yourself in relation to the sun's position throughout the day. Between your sun compass and circadian rhythm, you might think this getting-to-Michoacán thing might not be so tough after all. Then, it hits you: What if the sun isn't visible? *How will I make it to Michoacán?*

It's a good thing you have a backup plan.

Magnetic Marvels

Thanks to a mechanism that allows them to sense Earth's magnetic field, which is strongest at the North and South Poles, monarchs can stay on course. Weather doesn't matter. By **discerning** the magnetic field's *polarity* (which allows the monarchs to know which way is north and which is south) and *intensity* (which helps the butterflies "measure" their position in relation to the poles),

9

monarchs are able to remain on their flight path on days when the sun is nowhere to be seen. This ability also improves the monarchs' directional accuracy when the sun is shining bright.

One-Way Ticket, Please

As remarkable as the monarchs' **myriad** navigation techniques are, the butterflies appear not to use them on the return trip. In fact, the butterflies that made the long trip to Michoacán travel only a fraction of the way back. Instead, the female monarchs stop to lay their eggs, and the *next* generation resumes the journey. Sometimes, it takes two or three generations before the "grandchildren" and "great-grandchildren" of the ones that originally left return to the same place from which their ancestors originated.

Monarchs Win!

In some ways, the monarchs' remarkable navigational abilities match the capabilities of our own tools and technology. This allows the butterflies to successfully complete seemingly **arduous** journeys year after year. In other ways, monarchs exceed the limits of our most advanced, high-tech gadgetry by avoiding the need for repairs, updates, reboots, and—unless we're just not listening closely enough—asking for directions along the way.

EXERCISE 1 / WORD LIST

Use the context in which the word is used to determine what the word probably means. Write a brief definition in the space provided.

1. **arduous:** _____

   In some ways, the monarchs' remarkable navigational abilities match the capabilities of our own tools and technology. This allows the butterflies to successfully complete seemingly **arduous** journeys year after year.

2. **awry:** _____

   You might stop to ask for directions along the way, but that strategy is unpredictable and can go **awry** quickly.

3. **discern:** _____

   By **discerning** the magnetic field's *polarity* (which allows the monarchs to know which way is north and which is south) and *intensity* (which helps the butterflies "measure" their position in relation to the poles), monarchs are able to remain on their flight path on days when the sun is nowhere to be seen.

4. **innate:** _____

   For centuries, humans have used compasses to guide them to their destinations. Similarly, monarch butterflies use an **innate** sense—what scientists call a "sun compass"—to find their way to one specific forest in Michoacán.

5. **insurmountable:** _____

   The sun doesn't remain fixed in the sky, so it's not a stationary reference point. How is it possible for monarchs to overcome this seemingly **insurmountable** obstacle?

6. **labyrinthine:** _____

   Even a state-of-the-art GPS won't help you navigate the **labyrinthine** forest of intertwining trees once you're there, though.

7. **myriad:** _____

   As remarkable as the monarchs' **myriad** navigation techniques are, the butterflies appear not to use them on the return trip.

8. **orient:** _____

How can you fly in the correct direction if your critical point of reference moves all the time? It's a good thing you have *circadian rhythm*…to tell you how to correctly **orient** yourself in relation to the sun's position throughout the day.

9. **physiological:** _____

It's a good thing you have *circadian rhythm*—an "internal clock" that controls sleep/wake cycles and other **physiological** processes—to tell you how to correctly orient yourself in relation to the sun's position throughout the day.

10. **vibrant:** _____

The monarch butterfly—a primarily North American species adored for its **vibrant** black, orange, and white wings—does exactly that.

EXERCISE 2 / USING WORDS IN CONTEXT

Fill in the blank with the vocabulary word that best completes the sentence. In some cases, you may need to change the tense or form of a verb or the number of a noun.

innate	arduous	discern	vibrant	physiological
orient	labyrinthine	awry	myriad	insurmountable

1. In many bird species, males have _____ appearances that are used to attract the bland-colored females.

2. University researchers held an exhibit on _____ butterfly species in Australia and how to distinguish them.

3. How is it possible for ants to find their way through the _____ underground tunnels they construct?

4. Once the blizzard ended, the family had the _____ job of shoveling two feet of snow off their front porch.

5. It took a moment for the ladybug to _____ itself after the wind blew it across the backyard.

6. Because the book was handwritten on brittle, discolored paper, we were able to _____ that it was very old.

7. Our home restoration project went _____ when we discovered the basement walls were filled with termites.

8. Trying to memorize all the formulas in her algebra book seemed _____, but Alexa knew she had to try.

9. One _____ behavior of deer is to hide their fawns to protect them from predators.

10. Photosynthesis is a(n) _____ process in which light is converted to energy, which can then be used by the plant.

EXERCISE 3 / READING COMPREHENSION AND ANALYSIS

Select the best answers to the following questions based on a close and thorough reading of "The Marvel of the Monarch."

1. What purpose is served by the question "However, what if you decided to trust only your instinctive understanding of how to get [to your destination]?"

   A. It contrasts the monarchs' navigation system to GPS.

   B. It supports the argument that technology is superior to instinct.

   C. It emphasizes the difference between instinct and technology.

   D. It shows the arrogant human belief that intellect is superior to instinct.

   E. It leads into the main topic of the passage: butterfly navigation.

2. The author begins the third paragraph with a sentence about humans using compasses in order to

   A. capture the reader's attention using imagery.

   B. use a familiar concept to explain a new one.

   C. place the topic within the context of history.

   D. direct the reader's attention to a subtopic.

   E. emphasize the importance of travel.

3. The subhead "Monarchs Win!" most likely refers to what idea expressed in that paragraph?

   A. Monarchs that reach Michoacán can live and reproduce.

   B. Monarchs have navigational skills that are better than humans'.

   C. Monarchs annually travel farther than humans can.

   D. Monarchs use a new form of high-tech gadgetry.

   E. Monarchs get to Michoacán despite many obstacles.

4. Based on the passage, which of the following statements is FALSE?

   A. Monarchs' navigational abilities aren't learned.

   B. Humans use technology and external tools to navigate.

   C. It takes multiple generations of monarchs to return north.

   D. Circadian rhythm is essential to using the sun compass.

   E. Monarchs can navigate only when the sun is in the east.

5. Which segment could be eliminated without weakening the passage?

   A. "Butterfly GPS"

   B. "Here Comes the Sun Compass"

   C. "Magnetic Marvels"

   D. "One-Way Ticket, Please"

   E. "Monarchs Win!"

EXERCISE 4 / MAKING INFERENCES

Choose the best answer.

1. Which of the following would likely NOT be described as **labyrinthine**?

   A. instructions to assemble a desk with similar-looking parts

   B. a fast-moving interstate highway in the country

   C. a winding road that gets cars up a mountain

   D. the plot of a novel spanning 400 years

2. What could a historian use to best **discern** which crops were grown in the ancient village?

   A. images of food in still-life paintings

   B. contradictory information in old journals

   C. journals to publish her findings

   D. farming tools discovered in the old sheds

3. What would you most likely NOT do if faced with an **arduous** task?

    A. get the job done sooner than expected

    B. use devices that could help you

    C. consult someone who had done it before

    D. do some planning beforehand

4. Which of the following sentences shows the best example of the word **awry**?

    A. The awry worker made mistakes all of the time.

    B. We met at a hotel 400 miles awry because of a broken GPS.

    C. Everything went awry after the earthquake hit.

    D. Her long, angry glare at me from across the room made me feel awry.

5. What piece of information can be logically inferred from the following quotation from the passage?

    > "One monarch population makes an especially lengthy journey. These amazing insects travel from the northeastern United States to a forest in the Mexican state of Michoacán, on the country's southwestern coast, up to 3,000 miles away."

    A. Monarchs are the only insects that travel to Mexico.

    B. Monarchs go to Michoacán only because it is on the coast.

    C. Some monarch butterflies don't make a lengthy journey.

    D. All monarchs travel 3,000 miles to get to Michoacán.

EXERCISE 5 / ROOTS, PREFIXES, AND SUFFIXES

Answer the questions below that are designed to help you arrive at some conclusions about word families and origins.

1. Briefly define **innate** in your own words. What part of speech is **innate**?

   _____

   _____

   A. Given the meaning of the word, what does the prefix *in–* most likely mean?

      _____

      _____

   B. Given the meaning of **innate**, what does the root *nat* most likely mean?

      _____

      _____

   C. What other words share the same root as **innate**?

      _____

      _____

2. Briefly define **insurmountable** in your own words. What part of speech is **insurmountable**?

   _____

   _____

   A. Divide the word into syllables.

      _____

      _____

   B. In your own words, explain what aspect of the word's meaning each syllable provides. Use your knowledge of what the word means and anything you already know about the meanings of word parts to make a reasonable guess for each syllable. Feel free to consult a dictionary if you need to.

      _____

      _____

      _____

      _____

ALIENS AT ROSWELL?

"RAAF Captures Flying Saucer on Ranch in Roswell Region" ran the headline in the *Roswell Daily Record* on July 8, 1947. This story initiated the Roswell legend that still circulates today: A flying saucer crashed on a ranch outside of town, and the US military **surreptitiously** brought the debris and alien bodies back to the base. The following day, the public was told that what was discovered was a simple weather balloon.

How much of the story is true? Could events that occurred ten years apart, blended with the public's paranoia about UFOs, evolve into the myth we have today? On the other hand, is the government covering up an alien invasion? Both theories originated from a single incident, but then deviated.

On June 14th, a cattle rancher, Mac Brazel, was walking with his eight-year-old son and saw that something had fallen on his property. When he investigated the wreckage on July 4th, he found what he described as "rubber strips, tinfoil, a rather tough paper, and sticks." Two weather balloons had gone down in the area in the past, yet this debris looked completely different. Brazel had never seen anything like it before and neither had the local authorities. After being informed of the accident, the Roswell Army Air Force hurriedly retrieved the debris and brought it back to their base. The following day, they gave their official report: It was just a weather balloon.

Speculation began almost immediately: What really happened? What, exactly, did Brazel find? Was the **gullible** public easily misled by a lying government? Recently acquired information may hold the answers.

Brazel could have been right. What he saw may not have been a typical weather balloon. Declassified military reports describe a top-secret program called Project MOGUL. The items Brazel found may have been created by the United States for **reconnaissance** purposes. In 1947, in the middle of the Cold War, tensions were high between the United States and the Soviet Union—a communist dictatorship made up of Russia and other countries in Eastern Europe. Fearing nuclear war, the US created a system that could detect the sounds of aircraft and missiles.

The government developed balloons made of synthetic rubber, parchment, and plastic. These bear a striking resemblance to what Brazel found and, furthermore, would look unfamiliar to someone who had seen ordinary weather balloons before.

Even if the mysterious debris could be explained by Project MOGUL, what could account for the alien bodies people believe were found with the wreckage?

One explanation is that in the 1950s, the US military wanted to design better parachutes. To test the physical effects on falling pilots, the Air Force dropped mannequins resembling humans near Roswell. Witnesses may have seen army vehicles driving to the site to recover them and, **incredulously**, believed the government was taking away alien corpses. In fact, the mannequins likely inspired the image of aliens (called "Grey Aliens" or "Greys") that is prevalent in the modern media.

Then, in 1956, a KC-97G airplane crashed near Roswell. A fire in the cabin had killed the crew, and the bodies that were removed from the wreckage were barely recognizable as humans. When they were taken to be autopsied, even the nurses in the hospital thought the dead men were extraterrestrials. If a nurse could make such a mistake, couldn't the average citizen?

While the argument explaining the event through historical events may seem convincing, it contains several flaws. To begin with, if the government wasn't covering up an alien spacecraft, why did the Air Force remove the debris immediately? Furthermore, if the balloon were part of Project MOGUL, why did it take so long for the truth to be released, long after the Cold War had ended? Since the balloons had all been replaced with newer technology, why would **archaic** equipment be protected for so long?

Another major issue with this argument is that the three incidents described happened over the course of nine years. It certainly is possible for people to accidentally and **erroneously** meld several separate events into one. However, isn't it foolish to believe such a **convoluted** story as that one?

It is also impossible that the dummy drops and the airplane crash inspired the image of the Grey Aliens. That **depiction** of alien life appeared long before Roswell. In 1933, Swedish author Gustav Sandgren wrote the following in his work *Den okända faran* (*The Unknown Danger*):

> [...] the creatures did not resemble any race of humans. They were short...and their heads were big and bald, with strong, square foreheads, and very small noses and mouths, and weak chins. What was most extraordinary about them were the eyes—large, dark, gleaming, with a sharp gaze....

The description bears great similarity to how we generally depict an extraterrestrial—and came fourteen years before the Roswell incident.

Another event that often goes unreported and **corroborates** Brazel's story is the testimony of Mr. and Mrs. Wilmot, Roswell residents who saw a UFO in the sky around the same time as the crash, giving additional **credence** to Brazel's account. They described an aircraft that was "oval in shape, like two inverted saucers, faced mouth to mouth....glow[ing] as though light were showing through from inside," They also said it traveled at 400-500 mph across the sky without a sound. Could it be the object they saw was the same as Brazel's—or possibly an accompanying ship?

Arguments made on both sides of the Roswell incident are very convincing, which is why there is ongoing **discourse** among believers and skeptics. Are people's imaginations leading them to believe outlandish things? Or are secretive studies of extraterrestrial life being hidden from the public? Possibly, nobody will ever know the truth.

EXERCISE 1 / WORD LIST

Use the context in which the word is used to determine what the word probably means. Write a brief definition in the space provided.

1. **archaic:** _____

   Since the balloons had all been replaced with newer technology, why would **archaic** equipment be protected for so long?

2. **convoluted:** _____

   Another major issue with this argument is that the three incidents described happened over the course of nine years. It certainly is possible for people to accidentally and erroneously meld several separate events into one. However, isn't it foolish to believe such a **convoluted** story as that one?

3. **corroborate:** _____

   Another event that often goes unreported and **corroborates** Brazel's story is the testimony of Mr. and Mrs. Wilmot, Roswell residents who saw a UFO in the sky around the same time as the crash, giving additional credence to Brazel's account.

4. **credence:** _____

   Another event that often goes unreported and corroborates Brazel's story is the testimony of Mr. and Mrs. Wilmot, Roswell residents who saw a UFO in the sky around the same time as the crash, giving additional **credence** to Brazel's account.

5. **depiction:** _____

   It is also impossible that the dummy drops and the airplane crash inspired the image of the Grey aliens. That **depiction** of alien life appeared long before Roswell.

6. **discourse:** _____

   Arguments made on both sides of the Roswell incident are very convincing, which is why there is ongoing **discourse** among believers and skeptics.

7. **erroneous:** _____

   Another major issue with this argument is that the three incidents described happened over the course of nine years. It certainly is possible for people to accidentally and **erroneously** meld several separate events into one. However, isn't it foolish to believe such a convoluted story as that one?

8. **gullible:** _____

Was the **gullible** public easily misled by a lying government?

9. **incredulous:** _____

Witnesses may have seen army vehicles driving to the site to recover them and, **incredulously**, believed the government was taking away alien corpses.

10. **reconnaissance:** _____

The items Brazel found may have been created by the United States for **reconnaissance** purposes….Fearing nuclear war, the US created a system that could detect the sounds of aircraft and missiles.

11. **surreptitious:** _____

A flying saucer crashed on a ranch outside of town, and the US military **surreptitiously** brought the debris and alien bodies back to the base. The following day, the public was told that what was discovered was a simple weather balloon.

EXERCISE 2 / USING WORDS IN CONTEXT

Fill in the blank with the vocabulary word that best completes the sentence. In some cases, you may need to change the tense or form of a verb or the number of a noun.

discourse	gullible	convoluted	corroborate	surreptitious	reconnaissance
credence	depiction	archaic	erroneous	incredulous	

1. Liz got a failing grade on her assignment because of her _____ interpretation of the directions.

2. The tour guide's discussion of the mining industry was so _____ that it confused the visitors, who felt that they had not learned anything.

3. The _____ of Bigfoot in the television series did not match the description provided by the witnesses.

4. The scout went on a(n) _____ mission to learn the position of the German army.

5. The antagonist of the play lurked _____ in the shadows and eavesdropped on the two main characters' conversations.

6. Many _____ medical practices, such as the use of leeches, have been replaced with newer, more effective practices.

7. The presentation ended with a formal _____ between two geology experts who had differing opinions about the fossils.

8. Photographs and video recordings may _____ the idea that the chupacabra, a legendary goat-eating creature, actually exists.

9. Several _____ people believed the alien autopsy video was real, despite the overwhelming opinion that it was a hoax.

10. We were _____ when Mike said he had run a marathon in record time, especially since he didn't have any proof.

11. A manuscript from the 12th century lends _____ to the argument that King Arthur really existed.

EXERCISE 3 / READING COMPREHENSION AND ANALYSIS

Select the best answers to the following questions based on a close and thorough reading of "Aliens at Roswell?"

1. How is this passage organized?
   A. chronologically
   B. point and counterpoint
   C. cause and effect
   D. order of importance
   E. by topic

2. The author's intention of this passage is to
   A. convince the reader that extraterrestrials are real.
   B. reveal the information that was leaked about Project MOGUL.
   C. present two opposing sides on the Roswell debate.
   D. explain why aliens are portrayed the way they are.
   E. discredit Mac Brazel's and the Wilmots' stories.

3. Re-read the following excerpt from the passage:

   "How much of the story is true? Could events that occurred ten years apart, blended with the public's paranoia about UFOs, evolve into the myth we have today? On the other hand, is the government covering up an alien invasion? Both theories originated from a single incident, but then deviated."

   What is the purpose of the rhetorical questions?

   A. They capture the reader's attention.

   B. They introduce the opposing arguments to be discussed.

   C. They explain how the UFO myth began.

   D. They allude to the wreckage on Mac Brazel's property.

   E. They mimic the questions of the local authorities in Roswell in 1947.

4. When discussing the plane crash, the writer specifically mentions the opinions of the nurses in order to

   A. persuade the reader by stating the beliefs of specific individuals.

   B. use the opinions of people with expertise to strengthen an argument.

   C. distract the reader by introducing an unrelated topic.

   D. oversimplify the problem and easily discredit it.

   E. get the reader to adopt the popular opinion.

5. What would be the best alternative title for the passage?

   A. Mac Brazel's Famous UFO

   B. Truth of Roswell Discovered

   C. Roswell: Skeptics vs. Believers

   D. The Link between Roswell and Aliens

   E. The Government Conspiracy Called Roswell

EXERCISE 4 / MAKING INFERENCES

Choose the best answer.

1. If the computers in the lab are **archaic**, they most likely

    A. have outdated technology.

    B. don't work properly.

    C. are used frequently.

    D. need to be replaced.

2. Of the following, which is the best example of a **surreptitious** act?

    A. decorating a hall for a party

    B. listening to a friend's secret

    C. writing a novel by one's self

    D. sneaking into a movie theater

3. If students had to listen to a **convoluted** lesson, they would most likely

    A. believe that the teacher did not provide enough details.

    B. need to look up the information after class.

    C. understand the material and ace their test.

    D. link the information to other things they know.

4. Which of the following is the correct use of the word **credence**?

    A. We couldn't come to a credence on a restaurant, so we ordered take-out.

    B. There is no credence to the Bill of Rights in the Constitution.

    C. The evidence gave credence to the defendant's innocence.

    D. The credence of her comment made me disbelieve what she said.

5. Based on information in the passage, which of the following information can be inferred about Project MOGUL?

    A. The US was developing nuclear weapons at the time.

    B. The conflict between the US and Soviet Union began after WWII.

    C. The balloons were being used to spy on the Soviet Union.

    D. The balloons were based on alien technology obtained by the Soviet Union.

EXERCISE 5 / ROOTS, PREFIXES, AND SUFFIXES

Answer the questions below that are designed to help you arrive at some conclusions about word families and origins.

1. Briefly define **credence** in your own words. What part of speech is **credence**?

   _____

   _____

2. Briefly define **incredulous** in your own words. What part of speech is **incredulous**?

   _____

   _____

   A. What root do **credence** and **incredulous** share?

   _____

   _____

   B. List some other words that probably share the same root as **credence** and **incredulous**. Define each in your own words.

   _____

   _____

   _____

   _____

   _____

   _____

   C. Briefly explain in your own words how **credence** derives its meaning from its parts.

   _____

   _____

   D. Briefly explain in your own words how **incredulous** derives its meaning from its parts.

   _____

   _____

THE YEAR WITHOUT A SUMMER

[1] On April 10, 1815, English soldiers on the Indonesian island of Java prepared for battle when they heard the boom of cannon fire—or, at least, what they *thought* was cannon fire. Little did they know at the time that the sound didn't come from an advancing army, but instead, nature unleashing a **veritable** assault on the entire world. It would be one of the greatest catastrophes humanity had ever experienced.

[2] Mount Tambora had just erupted.

[3] The volcano, more than seven hundred miles away from the soldiers, produced the largest and deadliest eruption on record. The eruption pulverized and expelled two million tons of rock into the atmosphere. Scalding gas and ash flew down the mountain. Ash rained from the sky, and houses collapsed from the weight or burned. Entire villages were completely **decimated**. Roughly 10,000 people died from the immediate effects of the eruption alone. In the village of Tomboro, only 26 people survived, and tsunamis killed more than 4,000 others. Unfortunately, the longer-lasting consequences of the disaster would claim many more lives in the years that followed.

[4] The terrible **aftermath** and change in the environment proved much deadlier than the initial eruption itself. The dust and gas released into the atmosphere left the sky a thick haze, decreasing the amount of light reaching the earth. Worldwide temperatures dropped between 1.8 and 5.4° Fahrenheit. The cold continued into the following year, 1816, which became appropriately known as "The Year without a Summer."

[5] While such a seemingly small change in temperature may not appear significant enough to cause widespread problems, the drop was devastating to agriculture and, consequently, to the world economy. Globally, there was massive crop failure, including that of wheat and corn in Great Britain and rice in China. Several documents show that it snowed in the middle of summer in New England. Not only did farmers lose income, but the inadequate supply of food made it nearly impossible for the poor to feed their families. People were so desperate that they tried to **satiate** their hunger by eating nettles or clay. Begging rose drastically. People rioted in the streets, demanding solutions. Armed forces were sometimes brought in to break up violent demonstrations. Crime increased. Unfortunately, many of those who survived the starvation and malnutrition fell victim to disease.

[6] The connection between global cooling and disease may not be obvious, however. Climate changes and an alteration in the ecosystem can lead to the mutation of microorganisms, such as bacteria and viruses, many of which cause illness. An ecological disaster happened in the Bay of Bengal, India. The change in the atmosphere affected local weather patterns, which eliminated the yearly monsoons that people depended upon for growing their crops. There was severe drought when there should have been intense rain. The lower temperatures, combined with other Tambora-created factors, allowed the **pathogenic** bacteria that cause cholera to mutate and become much more dangerous. The fact that people were already weakened by a poor diet made them more **susceptible** to illness. The spread of cholera at this time was what many historians consider the first **pandemic**. It moved from Southeast Asia to other parts of the world. Cumulatively, the cholera outbreak, the starvation, and the direct effects of the eruption caused the deaths of an estimated 70,000-100,000 people.

[7] Surprisingly, though, there was a positive effect of "The Year without a Summer." Believe it or not, it led Mary Shelley to write *Frankenstein*.

25

[8] What, you might wonder, does a volcano have to do with a crazed, **maniacal** scientist and his monstrous creation?

[9] Geneva, Switzerland, was affected by the Mount Tambora eruption just as other places were. What would normally have been warm, dry weather was cold and rainy. Three Romantic-era writers—Lord Byron, Percy Shelley, and Mary Shelley—were vacationing at a resort there, but had to stay indoors for most of their trip. Being imaginative and inspired by the dismal setting, they decided to hold a contest. Who could write the best ghost story? Mary composed what would eventually become the most famous scene in *Frankenstein*:

> It was a dreary night of November that I
> beheld the accomplishment of my toils....
> [B]y the glimmer of the half-extinguished
> light, I saw the dull yellow eye of the
> creature open; it breathed hard, and a
> convulsive motion agitated its limbs....

[10] The gloomy atmosphere and the confinement to the villa helped create one of the most iconic works of horror!

[11] While novels, television shows, and movies sometimes are set in fictitious post-apocalyptic worlds with bleak, desolate conditions, few people know of the one that actually existed for a few years. The ash and debris that **emanated** from Mount Tambora may have remained within the region, but the indirect effects of the disaster were devastating. They transformed the entire world. Not only did the climate change, but hunger and disease also spread uncontrollably. Humanity struggled to **mitigate** the disastrous effects of the explosion, but those efforts were generally unsuccessful. The events of 1815-1816 certainly proved mankind's vulnerability to the **omnipotence** of nature and the destruction it can cause to civilization.

EXERCISE 1 / WORD LIST

Use the context in which the word is used to determine what the word probably means. Write a brief definition in the space provided.

1. **aftermath:** _____

   The terrible **aftermath** and change in the environment proved much deadlier than the initial eruption itself.

2. **decimate:** _____

   Ash rained from the sky, and houses collapsed from the weight or burned. Entire villages were completely **decimated**.

3. **emanate:** _____

   The ash and debris that **emanated** from Mount Tambora may have remained within the region, but the indirect effects of the disaster were devastating.

4. **maniacal:** _____

   What, you might wonder, does a volcano have to do with a crazed, **maniacal** scientist and his monstrous creation?

5. **mitigate:** _____

   Humanity struggled to **mitigate** the disastrous effects of the explosion, but those efforts were generally unsuccessful.

6. **omnipotence:** _____

   The events of 1815-1816 certainly proved mankind's vulnerability to the **omnipotence** of nature and the destruction it can cause to civilization.

7. **pandemic:** _____

   The spread of cholera at this time was what many historians consider the first **pandemic**. It moved from Southeast Asia to other parts of the world.

8. **pathogenic:** _____

   The lower temperatures, combined with other Tambora-created factors, allowed the **pathogenic** bacteria that cause cholera to mutate and become much more dangerous.

9. **satiate:** _____

Not only did farmers lose income, but the inadequate supply of food made it nearly impossible for the poor to feed their families. People were so desperate that they tried to **satiate** their hunger by eating nettles or clay.

10. **susceptible:** _____

The fact that people were already weakened by a poor diet made them more **susceptible** to illness.

11. **veritable:** _____

Little did they know at the time that the sound didn't come from an advancing army, but instead, nature was unleashing a **veritable** assault on the entire world. It would be one of the greatest catastrophes humanity had ever experienced.

EXERCISE 2 / USING WORDS IN CONTEXT

Fill in the blank with the vocabulary word that best completes the sentence. In some cases, you may need to change the tense or form of a verb or the number of a noun.

susceptible	aftermath	mitigate	pandemic	pathogenic	satiate
emanate	veritable	maniacal	decimate	omnipotence	

1. A loud buzzing noise _____ from the radio as some sort of static interfered with the signal.

2. The Great Fire of London _____ many structures that had been built in the Middle Ages.

3. The Ancient Greeks believed their deities had special abilities, but they did not believe the gods had _____ .

4. Doctor Reed was a(n) _____ expert on the Sasquatch legend, having studied the subject for over thirty years.

5. Few people foresaw the terrible _____ the war would have on society and the economy.

6. The pharmaceutical company created a drug to kill the _____ organism that caused an unusually high fever.

7. The press portrayed the research team as _____ conspiracy theorists until the group showed pictures of the man-made structures under the water.

8. We tried to _____ damage to the boat by covering it with a tarp, but the hail still ruined its beautiful finish.

9. The movie was about a worldwide _____ that turned half of the population into zombies.

10. Leaving a car unlocked with the windows down makes its contents _____ to theft.

11. Scott couldn't _____ his desire to know more about Roanoke, so he decided to take a trip to the site.

EXERCISE 3 / READING COMPREHENSION AND ANALYSIS

Select the best answers to the following questions based on a close and thorough reading of "The Year without a Summer."

1. Why does the author begin the passage with the story about the soldiers?

   A. to emphasize the magnitude of the eruption

   B. to place the events in a historical context

   C. to contrast man vs. man and man vs. nature

   D. to demonstrate how deceiving sounds can be

   E. to make the reader imagine being a soldier in 1815

2. Of the following, which is the most likely reason crime increased during "The Year without a Summer"?

   A. Greater emphasis was put on acquiring material wealth.

   B. England tried to oppress the people of Indonesia.

   C. The disaster was a good excuse to rebel against the elite.

   D. The people were poor and starving and had to steal to survive.

   E. The elite weren't giving up their stores of food to help the poor.

3. Which of the following was NOT an effect of the Mount Tambora eruption?

   A. A mutation of a bacterial strain led to cholera.

   B. Ash destroyed homes in Tomboro.

   C. Mary Shelley wrote *Frankenstein*.

   D. There were food shortages.

   E. Lake Geneva flooded.

4. Which of the following sentences would best fit into Paragraph 9?

   A. "John Polidori, who was with Lord Byron, was also inspired by the weather and later wrote *The Vampyre*."

   B. "Mont Blanc, which is featured in *Frankenstein*, is close to Geneva."

   C. "There were also reports of red snow falling in northern Italy."

   D. "The weather in Geneva is reflected in Mary Shelley's writing."

   E. "The house where Lord Byron stayed was called the Villa Diodati."

5. With which of the following statements would the author most likely DISAGREE?

   A. The welfare of the people depended on the yearly harvest.

   B. The bacteria strain probably wouldn't have mutated if the climate hadn't changed.

   C. The world looked like a post-apocalyptic landscape after the eruption.

   D. The novel *Frankenstein* might not have been written if it weren't for the Tambora eruption.

   E. The effects of the Mount Tambora eruption could have been prevented.

EXERCISE 4 / MAKING INFERENCES

Choose the best answer.

1. A building would be considered **decimated** if it

   A. is knocked down with a wrecking ball.

   B. is repaired by a construction company.

   C. has a strong foundation and sturdy walls.

   D. has statues stolen from the property.

2. In order to **mitigate** the effects of an illness, people might

    A. avoid situations in which they could get it.

    B. get treatment that would completely cure it.

    C. do things to intensify the symptoms.

    D. take medication to alleviate the symptoms.

3. Some people say that texting while driving is a **pandemic**, implying that the problem is

    A. extremely dangerous.

    B. within only a particular group of people.

    C. widespread or global.

    D. lessening over time.

4. Melissa might **satiate** her desire to socialize by

    A. staying home to play video games and read.

    B. dreading being embarrassed in public.

    C. going out to dinner with her friends.

    D. going to see her favorite movie for the fifth time.

5. What can you logically infer based on the following quotation from the passage?

    "The lower temperatures, combined with other Tambora-created factors, allowed the pathogenic bacteria that cause cholera to mutate and become much more dangerous."

    A. Before the eruption, cholera did not exist.

    B. Earlier strains of the cholera bacteria were not lethal.

    C. All pathogenic bacteria are harmless before mutation.

    D. Low temperatures caused the mutation of the cholera bacteria.

EXERCISE 5 / ROOTS, PREFIXES, AND SUFFIXES

Answer the questions below that are designed to help you arrive at some conclusions about word families and origins.

1. Briefly define **veritable** in your own words. What part of speech is **veritable**?

    _____

    _____

    A. Divide the word into its two most likely elements or components.

        _____

        _____

    B. You are probably already familiar with the second of these elements. What does it mean?

        _____

        _____

    C. List some other words that probably contain the first component of **veritable**. Define each in your own words.

        _____

        _____

        _____

        _____

        _____

        _____

    D. What does this word element most likely mean?

        _____

        _____

    E. Briefly explain in your own words how **veritable** derives its meaning from its parts.

        _____

        _____

2. Briefly define **pathogenic** in your own words. What part of speech is **pathogenic**?

    _____

    A. Divide the word into its two most likely elements or components.

        _____

        _____

B. List some other words that probably contain the first component of **pathogenic**. Define each in your own words.

_____

_____

_____

_____

_____

C. What does this word element most likely mean?

_____

_____

D. List some words that probably contain the second component of **pathogenic**. Define each in your own words.

_____

_____

_____

_____

E. What does this word element most likely mean?

_____

_____

F. Briefly explain in your own words how **pathogenic** derives its meaning from its parts.

_____

_____

WHO WAS KING ARTHUR?

[1] Most people have heard the legend of King Arthur, the wise monarch and the noble **paragon** of honor and chivalry, who pulled the sword Excalibur out of a stone to become king. He founded the Knights of the Round Table and courageously defended Britain against the Saxons. His fearless, adventurous knights went on heroic quests to retrieve the greatest relic of Christianity, the Holy Grail.

[2] Even though the story sounds like a myth, what if all or part of it were true? Did Arthur really exist? Tracing the evolution of the story over the past 1,600 years, it appears that Arthur was a real man, but maybe not the one we would recognize: He was actually a fifth- or sixth-century Roman commander.

[3] The first time "Arthur" is mentioned is in an early text, *De Excidio et Conquestu Britanniae*, by a British cleric named Gildas. He references a famous battle at Badon Hill, where a great Roman warrior fought off invading Saxons. That man's name was Aurelianus Ambrosius.

[4] The Romans took over Britain in 43 BCE. However, they began to withdraw from the area when the Saxons (pagans from parts of Europe that are now Germany and the Netherlands) attacked the empire, leaving the people to defend themselves. Ambrosius would have battled the invaders, under the banner of Christianity.

[5] Christianity is deeply rooted in British history and has been **intrinsic** to the Arthurian myth, even before Saint Augustine became the first Archbishop of Canterbury in 597 CE. By then, the southern part of Britain was largely Christian, so the war between the Britons and the Saxons was also one between the Christian belief in one God and pagan **polytheism**, with Arthur upholding the values of the former.

[6] Arthur appears next in an early ninth-century work called *Historia Brittonum* by a Welsh monk named Nennius. This time, Ambrosius is actually called Arthur, and he fights the Saxons with the blessing of God. Nennius also claims that, in this battle, Arthur kills 960 Saxons himself, which is not only false, but absolutely **preposterous**. While some facts may be true, Nennius started to change the story from history to fantasy, an act continued by another writer, Geoffrey of Monmouth.

[7] In his *Historia Regum Britannie*, the story continues to **deviate** from the original Gildas source. Geoffrey claimed to have found an old manuscript that he translated into Latin. He embellishes the text, though, adding new elements, including magic. Merlin, for example, predicts that the war between the Britons and the Saxons cannot end until Arthur's uncle becomes king. After he dies, the throne will then be passed to Uther, Arthur's father. Through Merlin's magic and **guile**, Uther seduces Igraine, the wife of another king. She gives birth to Arthur. After Uther's death, Arthur becomes king.

[8] Geoffrey then adds many other familiar details of the story. For instance, Arthur possesses Excalibur, although it is referred to as "Caliburnus" in the text. He marries Guinevere and, later, forms a company of knights. When he leaves Britain to fight, and later kill, the Roman emperor, Lucius Tiberius, Arthur's nephew Mordred falls in love with Guinevere and **usurps** the throne. Arthur battles and kills him, but is mortally wounded in the fight. He is taken to the island of Avalon and leaves his kingdom to Constantine.

[9] Geoffrey created the framework of the Arthurian myth we understand in the modern world, and subsequent stories added new details

to the narrative. In the twelfth century, Maistre Wace's *Roman de Brut* goes into detail about the **demeanors** of both Arthur and Guinevere, depicting Arthur as virtuous and chivalrous, and Guinevere as beautiful and kind. It's generally assumed that Arthur has his knights sit at the Round Table to prevent the appearance of favoritism: Since there is technically no "head," everyone can appear equal. According to Wace, however, Arthur inherits the Round Table from Guinevere's father. Another series of works, written by an unknown author in the thirteenth century and called the Vulgate Cycle, adds Sir Lancelot and his romance with Guinevere. It is also the first time the Holy Grail was associated with Arthur. The Holy Grail is supposedly the cup from which Jesus and the apostles drank at the Last Supper. Later, it was used by Joseph of Arimathea to collect Christ's blood after the crucifixion. The Vulgate Cycle says that Joseph's son brings the Grail to Britain, where it is held until Sir Galahad completes a quest and claims it.

[10] Similar stories are mentioned in the works of medieval writers Chreiten de Troyes and Robert de Boron, who was also the first to write that Excalibur was pulled from an anvil on top of a stone. Sir Thomas Mallory in *Le Morte d'Arthur* (1485) combines all of the elements into one complete work, but alters some: He makes Mordred Arthur's son, and Arthur does not pull Excalibur from an anvil, but from the stone itself.

[11] The tale of King Arthur is still fascinating centuries later, leading to many different **iterations** of the story in different forms. From books like T. H. White's *The Once and Future King*, to movies like *King Arthur*, to musicals like *Camelot*, the story changes to appeal to different audiences. Tracing the tale through the **plethora** of texts and back to the original source is difficult, and it's easy to dismiss Arthur as simply a legend. Only parts of the story are true. There was no Lancelot, Guinevere, or Merlin. The Round Table didn't exist, and Arthur didn't pull a sword from a stone. Arthur was just one brave man standing on a battlefield, a commander instead of a king, real instead of fiction.

EXERCISE 1 / WORD LIST

Use the context in which the word is used to determine what the word probably means. Write a brief definition in the space provided.

1. **demeanor:** _____

    In the twelfth century, Maistre Wace's *Roman de Brut* goes into detail about the **demeanors** of both Arthur and Guinevere, depicting Arthur as virtuous and chivalrous, and Guinevere as beautiful and kind.

2. **deviate:** _____

    While some facts may be true, Nennius started to change the story from history to fantasy, an act continued by another writer, Geoffrey of Monmouth. In his *Historia Regum Britannie*, the story continues to **deviate** from the original Gildas source.

3. **guile:** _____

    Through Merlin's magic and **guile**, Uther seduces Igraine, the wife of another king.

4. **intrinsic:** _____

    Christianity is deeply rooted in British history and has been **intrinsic** to the Arthurian myth, even before Saint Augustine became the first Archbishop of Canterbury in 597 CE.

5. **iteration:** _____

    The tale of King Arthur is still fascinating centuries later, leading to many different **iterations** of the story in different forms. From books like T. H. White's *The Once and Future King*, to movies like *King Arthur*, to musicals like *Camelot*, the story changes to appeal to different audiences.

6. **paragon:** _____

    Most people have heard the legend of King Arthur, the wise monarch and the noble **paragon** of honor and chivalry, who pulled the sword Excalibur out of a stone to become king.

7. **plethora:** _____

    Tracing the tale through the **plethora** of texts and back to the original source is difficult, and it's easy to dismiss Arthur as simply a legend.

8. **polytheism:** _____

By then, the southern part of Britain was largely Christian, so the war between the Britons and the Saxons was also one between the Christian belief in one God and pagan **polytheism**, with Arthur upholding the values of the former.

9. **preposterous:** _____

Nennius also claims that, in this battle, Arthur kills 960 Saxons himself, which is not only false, but absolutely **preposterous**.

10. **usurp:** _____

When he leaves Britain to fight, and later kill, the Roman emperor, Lucius Tiberius, Arthur's nephew Mordred falls in love with Guinevere and **usurps** the throne. Arthur battles and kills him, but is mortally wounded in the fight.

EXERCISE 2 USING WORDS IN CONTEXT

Fill in the blank with the vocabulary word that best completes the sentence. In some cases, you may need to change the tense or form of a verb or the number of a noun.

usurp	demeanor	intrinsic	plethora	preposterous
paragon	iteration	guile	deviate	polytheism

1. Katie is the _____ of honesty and won't lie under any circumstances.

2. Because the weather was so nice, the woman _____ from her normal routine and took a longer route home.

3. The Ancient Egyptians' religion was mostly _____, but at one point, they worshipped a single god named Aten.

4. One particular character in the novel has always had an unexplainable and _____ fear of heights.

5. Lily _____ the role of class president by spreading horrible lies about the previous one.

6. A surprising number of blockbuster movies are modern-day _____ of classic novels.

7. Even though Maria seems grumpy all of the time, once you get to know her, she has a kind and friendly _____.

8. Nobody respected Mr. Johnson because he became a millionaire through _____ and manipulation.

9. Even though hikers have come across large, human-like footprints, skeptics find the idea of Bigfoot _____.

10. The _____ of toys in the baby's crib indicated that his family spoiled him.

EXERCISE 3 / READING COMPREHENSION AND ANALYSIS

Select the best answers to the following questions based on a close and thorough reading of "Who Was King Arthur?"

1. Which of the following is NOT a logical reason the writer included the Arthurian myth in the first paragraph?

   A. to provide the specific version of the myth that will be discussed

   B. to illustrate the absurdity of the Arthurian myth

   C. to attract the reader's attention and engage him in the passage

   D. to present the mythical account of Arthur to be compared to the historical one

   E. to introduce aspects of the myth to be discussed in the passage

2. Re-read the following excerpt from the passage:

   > "The first time 'Arthur' is mentioned is in an early text, *De Excidio et Conquestu Britanniae*, by a British cleric named Gildas. He references a famous battle at Badon Hill, where a great Roman warrior fought off invading Saxons. That man's name was Aurelianus Ambrosius.
   >
   > The Romans took over Britain in 43 BCE. However, they began to withdraw from the area when the Saxons (pagans from parts of Europe that are now Germany and the Netherlands) attacked the empire, leaving the people to defend themselves. Ambrosius would have battled the invaders, under the banner of Christianity."

   Which would be the best improvement the author could make to this section?

   A. explain why the Saxons were migrating to Britain

   B. provide more information about Gildas's background

   C. remove the sentence beginning with "However, they began…"

   D. replace "Ambrosius" the second time it is used with "Arthur"

   E. create a better transition between the two paragraphs

3. Which of the following statements about Christianity CANNOT be found in or inferred from the text?

   A. The Christian religion came to Britain at the same time as the Holy Grail.

   B. The Saxons believed in many gods, but not the Christian one.

   C. King Arthur has always been associated with Christianity.

   D. Christianity in the Arthurian Legend began with a text by Gildas.

   E. Christianity existed in Britain before St. Augustine arrived.

4. Look at the following sentence carefully:

   "Merlin, sometimes called a magician or sorcerer, was vilified and made into the son of a demon; however, over time, he eventually became Arthur's trusted advisor."

   Where would the best place to include it be?

   A. Paragraph 3

   B. Paragraph 4

   C. Paragraph 5

   D. Paragraph 6

   E. Paragraph 7

5. Which of the following would be the best alternative title for the passage?

   A. The Forgotten Roman Soldier

   B. The Evolution of the King Arthur Legend

   C. King Arthur: King or Commander?

   D. Virtue and Chivalry in Arthurian Legend

   E. The Role of Christianity in Arthurian Myth

EXERCISE 4 / MAKING INFERENCES

Choose the best answer.

1. If a new scientific theory **deviates** from an older law, one could say that the theory

   A. has evolved from the earlier law.

   B. is the same as the original law.

   C. shares the same foundation as the law.

   D. has a completely different meaning than the law.

2. Shakespeare wrote that man is the "**paragon** of animals." He meant that humanity is

   A. different from animals.

   B. the worst type of animal.

   C. the most perfect animal.

   D. in the disguise of an animal.

3. Which of the following is an example of something being **usurped**?

   A. an understudy who takes the lead role in a play following an injury to the star

   B. a veteran who receives a medal of honor for bravery during combat

   C. a CEO who has been fired from a company for embezzlement

   D. a general who kills the president and takes control of a country

4. Which of the following is the best example of someone using **guile**?

   A. planning a road trip and arriving an hour early

   B. solving a riddle on a website

   C. passing a test after days of studying

   D. stealing money through a scam

5. Re-read the following excerpt from the passage:

   "The first time 'Arthur' is mentioned is in an early text, *De Excidio et Conquestu Britanniae*, by a British cleric named Gildas. He references a famous battle at Badon Hill, where a great Roman warrior fought off invading Saxons. That man's name was Aurelianus Ambrosius."

   What specific inference can be made by putting Arthur's name in quotation marks?

   A. Gildas is the only writer who calls Arthur by another name.

   B. Aurelianus Ambrosius was a Roman warrior.

   C. The man in Gildas's text isn't named Arthur.

   D. Arthur preferred to be known by a different name.

EXERCISE 5 / ROOTS, PREFIXES, AND SUFFIXES

Answer the questions below that are designed to help you arrive at some conclusions about word families and origins.

1. Briefly define **polytheism** in your own words. What part of speech is **polytheism**?

   _____

   A. Divide the word into its two most probable elements. Feel free to consult a dictionary or other source.

   _____

   B. List and briefly define some other words that contain the same first element as **polytheism**. What does this element most likely mean?

   _____

   _____

   _____

   _____

   C. List and briefly define some other words that contain the same second element as **polytheism**. What does this element most likely mean?

   _____

   _____

   _____

   _____

   D. Briefly explain in your own words how **polytheism** derives its meaning from its parts.

   _____

   _____

2. Briefly define **preposterous** in your own words. What part of speech is **preposterous**?

   _____

   _____

   A. Divide the word into syllables.

   _____

   _____

B. Which syllable indicates the part of speech? List some other words that share this syllable.

_____

_____

_____

_____

C. List some other words that contain the same first syllable as **preposterous**. What does this syllable most likely mean?

_____

_____

_____

_____

D. List some other words that contain the same second syllable as **preposterous**. What does this syllable most likely mean?

_____

_____

_____

_____

E. List some other words that contain the same third syllable as **preposterous**. What does this syllable most likely mean?

_____

_____

_____

_____

STONEHENGE

For over five thousand years, Stonehenge has stood quietly on England's Salisbury Plains. It has mystified archaeologists ever since its first excavation in 1620, and even now, has yet to reveal its secrets. How was the massive, Neolithic structure created without modern engineering, especially considering the largest stones weigh an average of twenty-five tons each? The smaller stones, weighing about four tons each, came from Wales, but how did they get to Stonehenge? Who constructed the monument, and what made it so meaningful that the ancient people devoted so much time and effort to building it? The evidence has yielded some potential answers—but has introduced even more questions.

What *Is* Stonehenge?

Stonehenge was originally a series of **concentric** rings made up of nearly 100 stones arranged around one center. There are two types of stone that can be **differentiated** from each other: the sarsens and the bluestones. The sarsens, the largest stones, are up to 30 feet high! The sarsens are arranged in "trilithons," which is the most **salient** and recognizable feature of Stonehenge. Each trilithon contains a pair of upright sarsens with a smaller stone, a "lintel," resting horizontally across the top.

The smaller bluestones are arranged individually, not in groups of three. They may seem **diminutive** by comparison, but even *they* weigh considerably more than a large pickup truck. The arrangement of the stones, particularly the sarsens, is truly a marvel, especially considering the limited technology available and the enormous effort it must have taken. How could Stonehenge even be possible?

How Was Stonehenge Built?

Stonehenge was created over a period of eight hundred years, beginning around 3000 BCE, **concurrent** with the building of the first pyramids in Egypt. The location underwent several periods of development, and to date, it isn't clear whether the final design was planned from the start or whether it evolved.

The site began as a simple "henge," a circular bank of dirt with a ditch in the center. A straight path leading to and from the henge was also created. The sarsens and bluestones weren't brought to the site for another 500 years. The sarsens were taken from the Marlborough Downs, roughly twenty miles away. Once brought to the site, the enormous stones had to be pulled upright. How was this feat accomplished using only primitive tools and methods? Scholars speculate that the stones were placed in holes and tipped vertically using timber counterweights. The lintels were likely raised to the top of the trilithons with wooden platforms or ramps made of dirt. Final adjustments to the stones' arrangement were made in 2200 BCE, and since then, Stonehenge has remained relatively unchanged.

One of the greatest wonders is how the bluestones arrived at the site. Even though they are smaller in size and easier to haul, how were they moved from the Preseli Hills in Wales, more than 140 miles away? The stones were likely carried down the River Avon using rafts, which were then unloaded; next, log rollers and rope were used to **facilitate** the transportation to Stonehenge. The movement of the stones was well organized and took a great deal of planning, but who could have been clever enough to complete this complicated task?

45

Who Were the Builders of Stonehenge?

Even during the Middle Ages, people speculated about its origin. Geoffrey of Monmouth, a 12th-century writer, wrote that Stonehenge had been constructed by Merlin, the wizard in the King Arthur legends. According to Geoffrey, Merlin magically positioned the stones. He supposedly built the monument as a burial site to honor warriors killed in battle, including some of Arthur's relatives. Considering how extraordinary the structure is, it seems as though it *had* to have been built by magic. Yet, while that tale is fascinating, it does not provide a reasonable answer.

The question remains as to who built Stonehenge. Historians and archaeologists make convincing arguments that it could have been built by multiple groups of people, especially since the construction of the **edifice** took so long. The most likely answer, however, is that the Druids built it. The Druid priests were familiar with astronomy. Considering that many Druid rituals and ceremonies were performed outdoors, Stonehenge could have had a special religious significance.

Why Was Stonehenge Built?

Even if the builders could be identified with certainty, *why* build Stonehenge? Could it have been designed as a calendar or astronomical map? It is true that the stones are **aligned** with the sun and other celestial bodies. Because of this specific arrangement, it's possible to **ascertain** that the architects were also astronomers. The stones are arranged to point out when the winter and summer solstices occur. On the summer solstice, the longest day of the year, sunlight travels down the path and across the rings. On the winter solstice, when the day is the shortest, the sun passes over three trilithons that are called the "great stones."

The most widely accepted theory, however, is that the site is a burial ground for **affluent** members of an old **patriarchal** aristocracy. Indeed, many graves, as well as ashes of cremated men between the ages of 20 and 45, have been found on the grounds. Could they be the warriors alluded to in Geoffrey's story?

Stonehenge is a modern tourist attraction, and millions of people have passed through it, oblivious to the complexity of the structure's design and construction. The ruins tell the story of early astronomers, centuries ahead of their time. The rocks' placement reveals the resourcefulness and ingenuity of engineers that led to the creation of a structure by seemingly impossible means. There are many unanswered questions, but one thing is certain—Stonehenge is a marvel and a testament to an ancient people.

EXERCISE 1 / WORD LIST

Use the context in which the word is used to determine what the word probably means. Write a brief definition in the space provided.

1. **affluent:** _____

   The most widely accepted theory, however, is that the site is a burial ground for **affluent** members of an old patriarchal aristocracy. Indeed, many graves, as well as ashes of cremated men between the ages of 20 and 45, have been found on the grounds.

2. **align:** _____

   It is true that the stones are **aligned** with the sun and other celestial bodies. Because of this specific arrangement, it's possible to ascertain that the architects were also astronomers.

3. **ascertain:** _____

   It is true that the stones are aligned with the sun and other celestial bodies. Because of this specific arrangement, it's possible to **ascertain** that the architects were also astronomers.

4. **concentric:** _____

   Stonehenge was originally a series of **concentric** rings made up of nearly 100 stones arranged around one center.

5. **concurrent:** _____

   Stonehenge was created over a period of eight hundred years, beginning around 3000 BCE, **concurrent** with the building of the first pyramids in Egypt.

6. **differentiate:** _____

   There are two types of stone that can be **differentiated** from each other....The sarsens, the largest stones,...are arranged in "trilithons"...The smaller bluestones are arranged individually, not in groups of three.

7. **diminutive:** _____

   The smaller bluestones...may seem **diminutive** by comparison, but even they weigh considerably more than a large pickup truck.

8. **edifice:** _____

Historians and archaeologists make convincing arguments that it could have been built by multiple groups of people, especially since the construction of the **edifice** took so long.

9. **facilitate:** _____

The stones were likely carried down the River Avon using rafts, which were then unloaded; next, log rollers and rope were used to **facilitate** the transportation to Stonehenge.

10. **patriarchal:** _____

The most widely accepted theory, however, is that the site is a burial ground for affluent members of an old **patriarchal** aristocracy. Indeed, many graves, as well as ashes of cremated men between the ages of 20 and 45, have been found on the grounds.

11. **salient:** _____

The sarsens are arranged in "trilithons," which is the most **salient** and recognizable feature of Stonehenge.

EXERCISE 2 / USING WORDS IN CONTEXT

Fill in the blank with the vocabulary word that best completes the sentence. In some cases, you may need to change the tense or form of a verb or the number of a noun.

salient	edifice	diminutive	concentric	patriarchal	align
ascertain	facilitate	concurrent	differentiate	affluent	

1. The chef pulled off the peel of the onion, which was in _____ layers around the center.

2. It was difficult to _____ whether they saw a sea monster since they weren't familiar with many species of marine life.

3. The largest oak trees in the forest are _____ compared to the gigantic redwoods in California.

4. The carpenter had to _____ the four pieces of the frame accurately to make a perfect square.

5. Even though Sara's notes weren't detailed, she recorded all of the _____ ideas in the chapter.

6. The enormous mansion and the expensive cars in the driveway were signs that the writer was very _____.

7. The fact that the lordship passed from father to son indicated that the society was _____.

8. In an effort to _____ communication with extraterrestrials, Doctor Thomas sent radio transmissions into space.

9. African elephants and Indian elephants can be _____ by the size and shape of their ears.

10. The pyramids of Giza are enormous _____ that are frequently visited by tourists.

11. Since they had the same group of friends and birthday, Emily and Amanda decided to have their parties _____ at the same place.

EXERCISE 3 / READING COMPREHENSION AND ANALYSIS

Select the best answers to the following questions based on a close and thorough reading of "Stonehenge."

1. The purpose of personification in the first two sentences of the passage is to

   A. emphasize the age and mystery of Stonehenge.

   B. highlight the ignorance of archaeologists.

   C. convey the solitude of the Salisbury Plains.

   D. stress the time between Stonehenge's construction and excavation.

   E. challenge the reader to learn Stonehenge's secrets.

2. The most likely reason the writer compares the weight of the bluestones to a pickup truck is to

   A. contrast modern technology to the "limited technology" of the Neolithic era.

   B. help the reader understand the weight of the bluestones.

   C. compare the length and height of the stones to a pickup truck.

   D. show the technology that would be used to build Stonehenge today.

   E. suggest that pickup trucks are modern marvels.

3. What sentence in the "How Was Stonehenge Built?" section best supports the idea that "it isn't clear whether the final design was planned from the start or whether it evolved"?

   A. "The site began as a simple 'henge,' a circular bank of dirt with a ditch in the center."

   B. "The sarsens and bluestones weren't brought to the site for another 500 years."

   C. "The sarsens were taken from the Marlborough Downs, roughly twenty miles away."

   D. "Once brought to the site, the enormous stones had to be pulled upright."

   E. "Final adjustments to the stones' arrangement were made in 2200 BCE, and since then, Stonehenge has remained relatively unchanged."

4. What information would REFUTE the statement that "log rollers and rope were used to facilitate the transportation [of the bluestones] to Stonehenge"?

   A. Log rollers may have been used to also transport the sarsens.

   B. It is unclear how the ropes would have functioned in the process.

   C. Some archaeologists say the stones were too heavy for log rollers.

   D. The wood was from the same timber used in other henges.

   E. The River Avon is far away from the Salisbury Plains.

5. With which statement would the writer most likely agree?

   A. The function of Stonehenge will never be determined.

   B. The bluestones may not have come from the Preseli Hills.

   C. Stonehenge is the most interesting Neolithic structure.

   D. Stonehenge couldn't have been built today.

   E. Modern technology is still superior to ancient technology.

EXERCISE 4 / MAKING INFERENCES

Choose the best answer.

1. If two trains are running **concurrently**, they

   A. leave the same station.

   B. travel in opposite directions.

   C. use the same tracks.

   D. have the same schedule.

2. Which of the following would be considered **concentric**?

    A. spokes of a wheel

    B. branches of a tree

    C. links of a chain

    D. layers of the earth

3. Which of the following would best represent the **salient** feature of a novel?

    A. a supporting character

    B. the central theme

    C. an unmemorable scene

    D. an allusion to another book

4. Of the following, which is NOT a correct example of the word **diminutive**?

    A. The diminutive boxer somehow knocked out his much larger opponent.

    B. The Chihuahua is one of the most diminutive dog breeds.

    C. The color of the shirt was diminutive compared to the brighter ones.

    D. The old church was diminutive compared to the new skyscrapers.

5. What can be inferred from the statement in the first paragraph of the "Who Were the Builders of Stonehenge?" section "Yet, while that tale is fascinating, it does not provide a reasonable answer"?

    A. The monument could not have been an ancient burial site.

    B. Geoffrey's entire historical information is false, and he is an unreliable source.

    C. Magic doesn't exist and couldn't have been used to build Stonehenge.

    D. There was no war in Britain when Stonehenge was built.

EXERCISE 5 / ROOTS, PREFIXES, AND SUFFIXES

Answer the questions below that are designed to help you arrive at some conclusions about word families and origins.

1. Briefly define **concentric** in your own words. What part of speech is **concentric**?

    _____

    _____

    A. Divide the word into its three most likely elements or components.

    _____

    _____

    B. You are probably already familiar with one or more of these elements. Given the meaning of the word, you should be able to guess at the ones you don't know. What does each mean?

    _____

    _____

    _____

    C. Briefly explain in your own words how **concentric** derives its meaning from its parts.

    _____

    _____

2. Briefly define **diminutive** in your own words. What part of speech is **diminutive**?

    _____

    _____

    A. Divide the word into syllables. Feel free to consult a dictionary or other source.

    _____

    _____

    B. Which syllable indicates the part of speech? List some other words that share this syllable.

    _____

    _____

    _____

C. Which syllable is most likely the root? What other familiar word(s) probably share this root? Briefly define each of these related words. Feel free to consult a dictionary or other source that explains word history in its definitions.

_____

_____

_____

_____

3. Briefly define **patriarchal** in your own words. What part of speech is **patriarchal**?

_____

_____

A. Divide the word into its three most likely elements or components.

_____

_____

B. Define each. Use whatever you already know about the meanings of roots, prefixes, and suffixes to make a reasonable guess. If you truly have no idea what a particular word element might mean, feel free to consult a dictionary or other source that explains word history in its definitions.

_____

_____

_____

C. List some words that most likely share each of the above word elements.

_____

_____

_____

_____

THE GREAT PYRAMIDS OF GIZA

Civilizations rise and fall, languages evolve, ancient religions vanish, and technology advances—yet, some things remain practically the same, **impervious** to time.

Five miles west of the Nile River and eight miles south of Cairo, Egypt, the marvel of the Great Pyramids of Giza remains almost **immutable**. The structures haven't changed much since their construction over four thousand years ago. How important were these complex, colossal structures to the ancient Egyptians, and what purpose did the monuments serve? Who built them, and how were the workers able to accomplish the task with limited equipment?

The questions have finally been answered, and the answers may surprise you.

The three Great Pyramids stand together in the middle of an area known as Giza. Their immense heights stand out **disproportionately** to anything else in the surrounding, flat desert. Their design is a tribute to the Egyptian sun god Ra, who, according to myth, sat on the top of a pyramid-shaped mound of earth. While they vary in size, the pyramids have the same essential form and composition. Each pyramid has a square base with triangular sides that meet at the top. The points of the square, fascinatingly enough, are aligned along an almost perfect North-South axis. The inner core of the pyramid was made from relatively inexpensive limestone mined from a local quarry, while the more impressive outer layer was created using limestone of a higher quality from farther up the Nile River. The capstone on the top was the most remarkable part; it was made of harder stone, perhaps granite, covered in gold or another expensive metal. Unfortunately, both it and the finer limestone were pilfered by thieves at the same time artifacts were stolen from the burial chambers deep inside the pyramids. Still, one can

only imagine looking up to the sky and seeing the shiny, **lustrous** tops reflecting the light of the sun.

The Great Pyramids were important to the ancient Egyptians and served to honor both their gods and the pharaohs, whom they **venerated** like deities. The Egyptians had a complex view of the afterlife, and they buried the deceased with the wealth and material goods needed in the next life. The pyramids themselves were also created to display the power and **opulence** of the pharaohs, leaving the ordinary citizens of Egypt, many of whom actually built the structures, to gaze at them in complete amazement.

Although not the *oldest* pyramids in Egypt (the oldest is the Pyramid of Djoser, built around 2630 BCE), the Pyramids of Giza are awe-inspiring. The largest of the three, the Great Pyramid, is the only **extant** structure of the Seven Wonders of the Ancient World. All of the others have been destroyed. Each of the three pyramids is unique and stands as a monument to one of three pharaohs.

The famed Great Pyramid, roughly 481 feet tall, was built during the reign of Khufu around 2550 BCE. The second pyramid, built around 2520 BCE by Khufu's son, Khafre, is slightly shorter, rising 448 feet above the desert sand. While Khafre's structure isn't as large as his father's, alongside it sits the mysterious sphinx, a limestone creature with the head of a human and the body of a lion. The third pyramid was commissioned by Menkaure, Kahfre's son, around 2490 BCE. Even though it is the smallest of the three pyramids, standing only 215 feet tall, the pyramid is no less impressive.

A popular myth is that slaves and foreigners built the pyramids, but this is false. The monuments were actually constructed by skilled and **adroit** Egyptian workers, directed by teams of architects and engineers. After uncovering a nearby workers' cemetery in Giza, archaeologists understood that the laborers were all Egyptian. Between 20,000 and 30,000 people built the Great Pyramids, and they were provided with adequate shelter and food—they were not slaves.

One of the greatest mysteries is how these three pyramids were created. With each block of stone weighing between 2.5 and 15 tons—the Great Pyramid, for example, consists of 2.3 million blocks—how would it have been possible to move the heavy stones, let alone get them all the way to the top?

The individual blocks were chiseled out in a quarry using copper tools. The blocks were then carried on the Nile River by boat. But what happened when the blocks reached the desert? Previously, it was thought that the blocks were moved on sledges transported along wooden rails; however, it is now understood that the sledges were pulled on sand alone.

Sand has an unusual property: When it is wet to a certain degree, it becomes smooth. As they moved the blocks for the pyramids, workers poured water on the sand in front of large, oxen-pulled sledges. The new, smooth surface had less friction, allowing the blocks of limestone to be moved more easily. The Egyptians were able to pull the stones from the river to the pyramid site using this technique.

The stacking of the stones was a tremendously difficult task, but one that these ancient engineers conquered. The workers didn't lift the blocks directly up the sides of the pyramids at a steep angle. Instead, they dragged the blocks along paths that increased in height and wrapped around the pyramids' sides. Although the paths were extremely long, the slope made it much easier for the workers.

While the Egyptian pyramids may **evoke** feelings of awe in visitors to Giza, what was once **inscrutable** is now better understood. The identity of the workers is no longer unknown, nor is the method by which the structures were erected. This greater knowledge, however, doesn't diminish the grandeur of the pyramids. Their imposing size and the history behind them will continue to amaze those interested in ancient wonders, as well as those merely mesmerized by the spellbinding **aesthetic** of the Great Pyramids of Giza.

EXERCISE 1 / WORD LIST

Use the context in which the word is used to determine what the word probably means. Write a brief definition in the space provided.

1. **adroit:** _____

   The monuments were actually constructed by skilled and **adroit** Egyptian workers, directed by teams of architects and engineers.

2. **aesthetic:** _____

   Their imposing size and the history behind them will continue to amaze those interested in ancient wonders, as well as those merely mesmerized by the spellbinding **aesthetic** of the Great Pyramids of Giza.

3. **disproportionate:** _____

   The three Great Pyramids stand together in the middle of an area known as Giza. Their immense heights stand out **disproportionately** to anything else in the surrounding, flat desert.

4. **evoke:** _____

   While the Egyptian pyramids may **evoke** feelings of awe in visitors to Giza, what was once inscrutable is now better understood.

5. **extant:** _____

   The largest of the three, the Great Pyramid, is the only **extant** structure of the Seven Wonders of the Ancient World. All of the others have been destroyed.

6. **immutable:** _____

   Five miles west of the Nile River and eight miles south of Cairo, Egypt, the marvel of the Great Pyramids of Giza remains almost **immutable**. The structures haven't changed much since their construction over four thousand years ago.

7. **impervious:** _____

   Civilizations rise and fall, languages evolve, ancient religions vanish, and technology advances—yet, some things remain practically the same, **impervious** to time.

8. **inscrutable:** _____

While the Egyptian pyramids may evoke feelings of awe in visitors to Giza, what was once **inscrutable** is now better understood. The identity of the workers is no longer unknown, nor is the method by which the structures were erected.

9. **lustrous:** _____

The capstone on the top was the most remarkable part; it was made of harder stone, perhaps granite, covered in gold or another expensive metal….[O]ne can only imagine looking up to the sky and seeing the shiny, **lustrous** tops reflecting the light of the sun.

10. **opulence:** _____

The Egyptians had a complex view of the afterlife, and they buried the deceased with the wealth and material goods needed in the next life. The pyramids themselves were also created to display the power and **opulence** of the pharaohs…

11. **venerate:** _____

The Great Pyramids were important to the ancient Egyptians and served to honor both their gods and the pharaohs, whom they **venerated** like deities.

EXERCISE 2 / USING WORDS IN CONTEXT

Fill in the blank with the vocabulary word that best completes the sentence. In some cases, you may need to change the tense or form of a verb or the number of a noun.

lustrous	venerate	extant	opulence	impervious	disproportionate
evoke	aesthetic	immutable	adroit	inscrutable	

1. Members of the drama club _____ Shakespeare and hold a festival in his honor every year.

2. The _____ gems in the woman's necklace immediately caught the thief's eye when he surveyed the room.

3. The rubber gloves were _____ to only one type of acid, so the chemistry teacher explained that it would not be safe to handle any others.

4. The pockets of the designer jeans contribute to the _____ design, but serve no practical purpose.

5. The number of books was _____ to the number of people in the class, so some students had to share.

6. It's pointless to have political debates with Jacob because his beliefs are _____, and he won't change his mind.

7. Both the lead detective and the psychiatrist on the case said the killer's motives were _____ and couldn't be understood unless he explained them himself.

8. The _____ of the dining room indicated that the family who lived there was very rich.

9. The sound of screeching violins in the background _____ a feeling of terror in the audience.

10. The audience looked in amazement at how _____ the magician was at deceiving everyone with his illusions.

11. The only _____ painting of the artist's is in the museum; the others were destroyed in a fire.

EXERCISE 3 / READING COMPREHENSION AND ANALYSIS

Select the best answers to the following questions based on a close and thorough reading of "The Great Pyramids of Giza."

1. The purpose of the short opening paragraph is to

    A. reveal the pyramids' connection to civilization, language, religion, and technology.

    B. imply that ancient Egyptian civilization, language, religion, and technology no longer exist.

    C. suggest how temporary human civilization is in the greater context of time.

    D. emphasize the age of the pyramids by contrasting them to other things with great longevity.

    E. indicate that without language, religion, and technology, basic civilization cannot exist.

2. According to the passage, which of the following statements about the pyramids is FALSE?

    A. The Sphinx was built at approximately the same time as the pyramids.

    B. The three pyramids were made completely of limestone.

    C. The Great Pyramid is one of the Seven Wonders of the Ancient World.

    D. The pyramids have square bases and triangular sides.

    E. The smallest pyramid of the three was commissioned by Menkaure.

3. Which of the following main ideas unites this passage with the one called "Stonehenge"?

   A. Both ancient civilizations built incredible structures using primitive technology.

   B. Religion inspired the construction of the two amazing building projects.

   C. We will never understand everything about the ancient technologies they used.

   D. Monarchs at both sites had monuments built to demonstrate their power and wealth.

   E. Building materials for both types of construction were transported over water.

4. Which of the following would be a way to improve the paragraph that begins with "Sand has an unusual property…"?

   A. mention the distance the blocks had to be pulled

   B. discuss other ways the unique property of sand is useful

   C. briefly explain how friction would hinder movement

   D. explain that the desert heat made moving the blocks more difficult

   E. detail the length of time it took to build the pyramids

5. With which statement would the author most likely agree?

   A. Limestone was the only stone the Egyptians had available to build the pyramids.

   B. Pyramids were built only by the ancient Egyptian civilization.

   C. The pyramids wouldn't have been built if it weren't for the devotion to Ra.

   D. The pyramids are as impressive today as when they were built.

   E. All of the pyramids of Giza have around 2.3 million blocks.

EXERCISE 4 / MAKING INFERENCES

Choose the best answer.

1. Which of the following is a correct use of the word **venerate**?

   A. The toddler venerated her mother by throwing an angry fit about a punishment.

   B. Carly venerated her love of dogs by becoming a vet immediately after graduation.

   C. The writer venerated a mysterious woman in his poetry and detailed her virtues.

   D. Jon venerated the music of his favorite band, so he listened to a different group.

2. Which of the following could be best described as **immutable**?

    A. a car that has run out of gas on the side of the road

    B. a tool that can be used for multiple purposes

    C. a possible outcome that can't be achieved yet

    D. a law that can't be questioned or broken

3. If there is only one **extant** restaurant in town, it can be inferred that

    A. the restaurant specializes in one type of food.

    B. the food at the other restaurants is terrible.

    C. other restaurants are no longer there.

    D. prices are higher than at other restaurants.

4. An **inscrutable** facial expression would likely allow Janet to

    A. be a good model for a painting.

    B. become a famous actress.

    C. show her emotions well.

    D. lie convincingly.

5. In the passage, what phrase near **impervious** helps you infer its meaning?

    A. "rise and fall"

    B. "languages evolve"

    C. "to time"

    D. "practically the same"

EXERCISE 5 / ROOTS, PREFIXES, AND SUFFIXES

Answer the questions below that are designed to help you arrive at some conclusions about word families and origins.

1. Briefly define **immutable** in your own words. What part of speech is **immutable**?

   _____

   A. Given what you already know about prefixes, suffixes, and roots, divide **immutable** into its most likely elements.

   _____

   _____

   B. Explain the meaning of this word's prefix and suffix, both of which you are probably already familiar with.

   _____

   _____

   C. What other familiar words share the same root as **immutable**? Define each in your own words.

   _____

   _____

   _____

   D. Given the meaning of **immutable** and the related words, what does their common root most likely mean?

   _____

   _____

2. Briefly define **inscrutable** in your own words. What part of speech is **inscrutable**?

   _____

   A. Divide the word into its three most likely elements or components.

   _____

   _____

   B. You should be familiar with the first and third of these elements. What do they mean?

   _____

   _____

C. List some other words that probably contain the second component, the root, of **inscrutable**. Define each in your own words.

_____

_____

_____

D. What does this word element most likely mean?

_____

_____

WHO WROTE "SHAKESPEARE"?

Despite being revered as the greatest English playwright and poet of all time, not much is known about William Shakespeare, commonly known as "the Bard." We do know that a man, whom we will call "Shakspere," as opposed to the writer, "Shakespeare," was born in 1564 to a leatherworker-merchant and his wife. He lived in Stratford-upon-Avon, where he **purportedly** attended the local grammar school, The King's New School. While there is no written proof of his enrollment, he would have gone there for free because his father was on the town council. He became an actor and business partner in the Lord Chamberlain's Men (also "The King's Men") and helped build the Globe Theatre. But was he a writer, specifically of the 37 plays and 154 sonnets **ascribed** to him?

Very little documentary evidence about the Bard exists. Very little links the actor's name to the famous works. A few historians and literary scholars have begun to wonder if maybe what we thought we knew isn't true. What if Shakespeare weren't Shakspere, but someone else?

There has rarely been such a **factious** debate in the field of literature, with each side viciously attacking the other. Scholars on one side of the argument (Stratfordians) are offended by what they see as the **audacity** of conspiracy theorists, who deliberately ignore or misinterpret the facts. The opposition (Anti-Stratfordians) claims that many people have an **inveterate** acceptance of Shakespeare's identity despite little being known about him. Several famous writers have also been among the skeptics, including Nathaniel Hawthorne, Walt Whitman, and Mark Twain. Was Shakespeare really the man from Stratford-upon-Avon, or is the name a **pseudonym**? Four subjects that frequently arise in the debate are Shakspere's handwriting, name, knowledge, and literacy.

One would think that a man as **prolific** a writer as Shakespeare, who wrote so many plays, would have left behind handwritten journals or manuscripts; but the only writing sample that may have been penned by the Bard is a segment of the play *The Book of Sir Thomas More*. Handwriting experts have compared the writing on the manuscript to six legal documents that contain Shakespeare's signature, and there is disagreement on whether the samples are similar. Some Anti-Stratfordians have suggested that the printer, not the author, wrote the manuscript, rendering this comparison completely pointless.

Not only has the handwriting been questioned, so has the actual name. Unfortunately, the name "Shakespeare" didn't appear until it was used on the 1623 *First Folio*, a collection of Shakespeare's plays compiled seven years after his death. The actor from Stratford-upon-Avon, Shakspere, never spelled his name with the extra vowels. Stratfordians point out, however, that there was no standard spelling in the day, and the names on the documents themselves are **dissimilar**. The actual signature was spelled *five* different ways: Shakp, Shaksper, Shakspe, Shakspere, and Shakspeare.

Knowledge, or what information the playwright would have been exposed to, is another debated topic. How could Shakspere have written the plays if he didn't have a university education? Shakspere wouldn't have attended any school other than The King's New School. He also hadn't spent time abroad or had first-hand knowledge of aristocratic life. Furthermore, a lot of the sources the Bard used for his works were in Latin and had not yet been translated into English. Could Shakepere and Shakespeare have been the same person?

The answer that the Stratfordians put forth is, **unequivocally**, "yes." The boys attending the

65

grammar school would have learned both Latin and Greek. The stories that Shakespeare adapted into plays might have been ones that he studied. Additionally, even if he had never been abroad, he could have gathered specific information from books, or maybe just through casual conversations with friends who had traveled. As for the depiction of aristocratic life, many historians indicate that his portrayal of how royalty and nobility act is inaccurate. The person who wrote the plays might not have been an aristocrat himself. Shakspere would, once again, seem a likely candidate for being the author.

The question of literacy, however, remains. If enrollment records can't show that Shakspere attended the grammar school, what proof is there that he could read? His will did not include any mention of books, which were valuable at that time. Would one of the greatest writers who ever lived not have owned any books? There is also no evidence that Shakspere's father or daughters were literate, which would make him the one person in three generations of the family who could read. His daughter Judith, for example, couldn't write her own name, but signed with an "X." Anti-Stratfordians find this fact suspicious and proof that someone other than Shakspere authored the plays.

But who?

If Shakspere was not the famous writer, who was? Suggestions have ranged from Christopher Marlowe, a contemporary playwright, to Francis Bacon, an English philosopher—but the candidate that Anti-Stratfordians have supported the most is Edward de Vere, the 17th Earl of Oxford. The British theater of the time was not a place of sophistication and refinement as it is today. In their opinion, Oxford would have avoided the **impropriety** of being a playwright by writing under a pseudonym. The Stratfordians, however, point out that Oxford was already openly involved in the theater, had his own company, and would not have felt ashamed at being associated with writing plays or acting. Furthermore, Oxford died in 1604, several years before Shakespeare stopped writing. If the Anti-Stratfordians are correct, the dates we believe the plays were written would be wrong, as would the entire history of the writer's career as we know it.

In the great Shakespeare-authorship debate, both sides make convincing arguments. Can it be possible that Shakspere of Stratford-upon-Avon wrote the most famous plays in the English language? Is the idea that a middle-class actor without much formal education could be the famous Bard **ludicrous**, or absolutely amazing? With little documentary evidence available, there is unlikely to be a conclusion any time soon. For at least a little while longer, Shakespeare's life will be shrouded in mystery.

EXERCISE 1 / WORD LIST

Use the context in which the word is used to determine what the word probably means. Write a brief definition in the space provided.

1. **ascribe:** _____

But was he a writer, specifically of the 37 plays and 154 sonnets **ascribed** to him?

2. **audacity:** _____

Scholars on one side of the argument (Stratfordians) are offended by what they see as the **audacity** of conspiracy theorists, who deliberately ignore or misinterpret the facts.

3. **dissimilar:** _____

Stratfordians point out, however, that there was no standard spelling in the day, and the names on the documents themselves are **dissimilar**. The actual signature was spelled five different ways: Shakp, Shaksper, Shakspe, Shakspere, and Shakspeare.

4. **factious:** _____

There has rarely been such a **factious** debate in the field of literature, with each side viciously attacking the other.

5. **impropriety:** _____

The British theater of the time was not a place of sophistication and refinement as it is today. In their opinion, Oxford would have avoided the **impropriety** of being a playwright by writing under a pseudonym.

6. **inveterate:** _____

The opposition (Anti-Stratfordians) claims that many people have an **inveterate** acceptance of Shakespeare's identity despite little being known about him.

7. **ludicrous:** _____

Is the idea that a middle-class actor without much formal education could be the famous Bard **ludicrous**, or absolutely amazing?

8. **prolific:** _____

One would think that a man as **prolific** a writer as Shakespeare, who wrote so many plays, would have left behind handwritten journals or manuscripts…

9. **pseudonym:** _____

Was Shakespeare really the man from Stratford-upon-Avon, or is the name a **pseudonym**?

10. **purported:** _____

He lived in Stratford-upon-Avon, where he **purportedly** attended the local grammar school, The King's New School. While there is no written proof of his enrollment, he would have gone there for free because his father was on the town council.

11. **unequivocal:** _____

Furthermore, a lot of the sources the Bard used for his works were in Latin and had not yet been translated into English. Could Shakepere and Shakespeare have been the same person?

The answer that the Stratfordians put forth is, **unequivocally**, "yes." The boys attending the grammar school would have learned both Latin and Greek.

EXERCISE 2 / USING WORDS IN CONTEXT

Fill in the blank with the vocabulary word that best completes the sentence. In some cases, you may need to change the tense or form of a verb or the number of a noun.

factious	impropriety	ludicrous	inveterate	purported	ascribe
audacity	prolific	dissimilar	pseudonym	unequivocal	

1. Even though most people wouldn't hear the difference, two different cellos may sound _____ to a trained musician.

2. In order to conceal her identity, Charlotte Brontë used the _____ "Currer Bell."

3. Teri became a(n) _____ supporter of the local football team, despite the fact that they never won the Super Bowl.

4. Rembrandt was a(n) _____ artist during his lifetime because he produced many paintings.

5. The _____ decision to promote Claire was based on the excellence she demonstrated in her job.

6. The candidate was doing well in the polls until the instance of financial _____ ruined his chances.

7. The _____ update to the office computers must not have happened because we were still having trouble connecting to the Internet.

8. Even though the photograph was _____ to Jen, it was obvious that David took the picture.

9. The conversation transformed into a(n) _____ argument that made both people storm out of the room.

10. Gabriel couldn't believe the _____ of his sister when she asked him for money and then wasted it on clothes.

11. The thought that the campers saw a monster in the woods seemed _____ to the police officers filing the report.

EXERCISE 3 / READING COMPREHENSION AND ANALYSIS

Select the best answers to the following questions based on a close and thorough reading of "Who Wrote 'Shakespeare'?"

1. The author's intent is to

   A. provide biographical information on Shakspere's life.

   B. persuade the reader that the Stratfordians are correct.

   C. persuade the reader that the Anti-Stratfordians are correct.

   D. present an unbiased explanation of both sides of the argument.

   E. explain why the Earl of Oxford is most likely the actual Shakespeare.

2. Why is it significant that Shakspere's father was a member of the town council?

   A. It is surprising because he was also a leatherworker and merchant.

   B. This fact contradicts what literary scholars had believed for years.

   C. The comment suggests that Shakspere wasn't a member of the middle class.

   D. It explains why Shakspere had an understanding of the aristocratic life.

   E. It makes Shakspere's attendance at The King's New School more plausible.

3. Which is the best paraphrase of this excerpt from the passage?

   "Some Anti-Stratfordians have suggested that the printer, not the author, wrote the manuscript, rendering this comparison completely pointless."

   A. Anti-Stratfordians believe the handwriting on the manuscript isn't Shakespeare's, so it can't be compared to his signatures.

   B. It is pointless to compare the manuscript to Shakespeare's various signatures on legal documents.

   C. Printers rewrote all plays in their own handwriting and threw out the original manuscripts.

   D. The manuscript can't be compared to the signatures because it shows a different style of writing.

   E. Only Anti-Stratfordians believe that the manuscript was written by the printer and not by Shakespeare.

4. Which of the following is NOT an argument the author uses to prove that *Shakspere* and *Shakespeare* are different people?

   A. There is no proof that Shakspere went to grammar school.

   B. Everyone else in Shakspere's family was illiterate.

   C. Edward de Vere was actually Shakespeare.

   D. The handwriting on the *Sir Thomas More* play does not match Shakespeare's signature.

   E. Shakspere never signed his name "Shakespeare."

5. What would be the best alternative title for the passage?

   A. Stratfordians vs. Anti-Stratfordians

   B. The Identity of the Bard Finally Revealed

   C. Rethinking Shakespeare's Identity

   D. All that We Know about Shakespeare

   E. Shakespeare Is Shakspere

EXERCISE 4 / MAKING INFERENCES

Choose the best answer.

1. Which of the following is NOT an example of **impropriety**?

   A. leaving a party without saying goodbye

   B. interrupting someone in a conversation

   C. shoplifting from a store

   D. forgetting to respond to an email

2. You might **ascribe**

   A. a font to a document.

   B. an idea to a famous philosopher.

   C. an image in a collage.

   D. a book with symbolism.

3. Which of the following is an example of someone or something being **prolific**?

   A. a businessman who is very wealthy

   B. a tree producing a lot of fruit

   C. an organization that gives money to charity

   D. an architect designing the world's tallest skyscraper

4. A plan that is **factious** would most likely

   A. separate people into groups.

   B. lead to competition.

   C. create a state of chaos.

   D. cause an argument.

5. Which of the following would NOT be a logical inference you could make about the passage?

   A. The author firmly believes that the points made by the Stratfordians are correct.

   B. Shakespeare is now respected as the greatest playwright who ever lived.

   C. It will never be known whether Shakspere wrote the plays we associate with Shakespeare.

   D. The date of the Earl of Oxford's death makes it almost impossible for him to be Shakespeare.

EXERCISE 5 / ROOTS, PREFIXES, AND SUFFIXES

Answer the questions below that are designed to help you arrive at some conclusions about word families and origins.

1. Briefly define **impropriety** in your own words. What part of speech is **impropriety**?

   _____

   _____

   A. List and briefly define some other words that contain the same suffix as **impropriety**. What is the apparent function of this suffix?

   _____

   _____

   _____

   _____

   _____

   B. You probably already know what the prefix means. List a few other words that use this prefix and explain briefly what it means.

   _____

   _____

   _____

   C. What is the apparent root of **impropriety**? List a few other words that contain this root. Given the meaning of the word and its prefix and suffix, what does this root most likely mean?

   _____

   _____

   _____

   _____

2. Briefly define **pseudonym** in your own words. What part of speech is **pseudonym**?

   _____

   _____

   A. Divide the word into its two most probable elements. Feel free to consult a dictionary or other source.

   _____

   _____

B. Define *pseudoscience*, a word that contains the same first element as **pseudonym**. What does this element most likely mean?

_____

_____

_____

C. List and briefly define some other words that contain the same second element as **pseudonym**. What does this element most likely mean?

_____

_____

_____

_____

_____

_____

_____

_____

_____

D. Put the two elements together and briefly explain what **pseudonym** literally means.

_____

_____

_____

"NESSIE"

Every year, about a million people travel to Loch Ness, one of the most popular tourist spots in Scotland. They stand on the bank of the loch (the Scottish Gaelic word for "lake"), ready with their phones and cameras, hoping to catch a glimpse of the Loch Ness Monster, otherwise known as "Nessie."

Nessie has developed quite a reputation. While she tends to be an elusive creature, swimming deep within the murky water, many people have spotted her on the rare occasion she's come to the surface. Most accounts describe her as a colossal beast with a long neck, one or more humps, and flippers. There are many **conjectures** about what she is, but it is commonly thought that she is a plesiosaur, an aquatic dinosaur that supposedly went extinct over 65 million years ago. There are, of course, skeptics who think that Nessie is just a myth **fabricated** to attract tourists. Could Nessie be one the greatest hoaxes of all time, or is there truly a mysterious creature living in Loch Ness?

"Strange Spectacle on Loch Ness"
The more modern-day history of Nessie began when a road was constructed next to the loch. It made the lake more accessible but possibly roused Nessie with the sounds of blasting and drilling. On May 2, 1933, a local newspaper, the *Inverness Courier*, printed an article titled "Strange Spectacle on Loch Ness." An anonymous but "well-known businessman" and his wife were driving past the lake and noticed a disturbance in the water. When they stopped, they saw a "creature…milling and plunging for fully a minute…[before] taking the final plunge and sen[ding] out waves that were big enough to have been caused by a passing steamer." The couple described the beast as large with "a body resembling that of a whale." The story also noted that members of the local **populace**

had reported similar sightings. Local fishermen witnessed something initially believed to be a seal or porpoise; however, as the newspaper pointed out, neither porpoises nor seals had been spotted there before.

The story **elicited** several testimonies by others who claimed to have seen the monster. The *Daily Mail*, a newspaper in London, wanted proof and sent Marmaduke Wetherell, a big-game hunter, to search for the creature.

The Hunter and the Hippopotamus Foot
In December 1933, Wetherell scoured Loch Ness. After a few days, he claimed to have found footprints near the lake; he made plaster casts and sent them to the Natural History Museum in London. After analysis, the museum declared that the footprints had been made with a dried hippopotamus foot that had been used as an umbrella stand—feet from hippos and elephants were common household decorative items at the time. Furthermore, the finding was **incongruous** with other reports saying the monster had flippers, not feet. Wetherell was publicly **derided** and humiliated, but he eventually got his revenge: a deception so cunning that it wasn't discovered until sixty years later.

The Famous Fake Photo
In 1934, shortly after Wetherell's embarrassment, the *Daily Mail* received a photograph from Dr. Robert Kenneth Wilson, a well-known physician. He claimed that he went to the lake to take images of birds. When he heard something in the water, he went to investigate and encountered the creature. **Fortuitously**, he had his camera with him and became the first person to capture Nessie on film. Since then, the image has been reproduced innumerable times and is called "The Surgeon's Photo."

In 1994, however, the image was revealed to be fake. Christian Spurling, the stepson of Mr. Wetherell, confessed that the object in the photo was actually a toy submarine with an attachment above the water made to look like a head and neck. Wetherell, the ridiculed con man, had concealed his own involvement by using the respected Wilson to sell the image to the paper. In order to avenge the damage to his reputation, Wetherell came up with this **ruse** and fooled the entire world!

Even though the faked photo may have been **deleterious** to any belief in the monster in the loch, there are still other peculiarities about Nessie that can't be explained.

Picts, Pictures, and Prayers

Although Nessie may not have made it into the press until 1933, stories about her predate the newspaper article by centuries. The Picts, a group of people who lived in Scotland before the Roman invasion, drew images that bore a striking resemblance to the monster. The Picts also believed that water-horses, or water-kelpies, would lure people to the water and drown them. Could these tales be considered just legends and superstition, or is there some truth to them?

If one is unwilling to believe in the superstitions of an ancient people, there is another source that may be more **credible**. A 7th- to 8th-century abbot, Adomnán, wrote about St. Columba's trip to Scotland in 565 CE. Columba encountered a creature that was attempting to eat a swimmer in the Ness River, which connects to the lake. After praying to God, he forced the monster back into the water. Could the monster have been Nessie or one of her ancestors?

The Science of Sonar

Considering the popularity of the Nessie story, many scientists doing research bring advanced technology with them. Groups from Oxford, Cambridge, and the University of Birmingham have used sonar in their studies. While the findings were "inconclusive," the groups did discover large moving objects in the water that could not be identified. Later, in 1975, a group of researchers from the Academy of Applied Sciences in Vermont searched Loch Ness. Their results were even more interesting. Using underwater photography in addition to sonar, they captured an image of what appeared to be a flipper. Some scientists were skeptical about it. Others have passionately **expounded** that it is definite proof Nessie exists.

Scientists and curious visitors regularly search the area, hoping to have their own personal encounter with Nessie. Some have claimed to have spotted her, and a few lucky ones have even taken convincing photos and videos. Does the famous loch harbor a remnant of the world that existed 65 million years ago? Could Nessie be a hoax, or perhaps some everyday thing mistaken for a monster? For now, though, she will just have to remain a mystery.

EXERCISE 1 / WORD LIST

Use the context in which the word is used to determine what the word probably means. Write a brief definition in the space provided.

1. **conjecture:** _____

   There are many **conjectures** about what she is, but it is commonly thought that she is a plesiosaur, an aquatic dinosaur that supposedly went extinct over 65 million years ago.

2. **credible:** _____

   If one is unwilling to believe in the superstitions of an ancient people, there is another source that may be more **credible**.

3. **deleterious:** _____

   Even though the faked photo may have been **deleterious** to any belief in the monster in the loch, there are still other peculiarities about Nessie that can't be explained.

4. **deride:** _____

   Wetherell was publicly **derided** and humiliated, but he eventually got his revenge: a deception so cunning that it wasn't discovered until sixty years later.

5. **elicit:** _____

   The story **elicited** several testimonies by others who claimed to have seen the monster.

6. **expound:** _____

   Some scientists were skeptical about it. Others have passionately **expounded** that it is definite proof Nessie exists.

7. **fabricate:** _____

   There are, of course, skeptics who think that Nessie is just a myth **fabricated** to attract tourists. Could Nessie be one the greatest hoaxes of all time, or is there truly a mysterious creature living in Loch Ness?

8. **fortuitous:** _____

   He claimed that he went to the lake to take images of birds. When he heard something in the water, he went to investigate and encountered the creature. **Fortuitously**, he had his camera with him and became the first person to capture Nessie on film.

9. **incongruous:** _____

Furthermore, the finding was **incongruous** with other reports saying the monster had flippers, not feet.

10. **populace:** _____

The couple described the beast as large with "a body resembling that of a whale." The story also noted that members of the local **populace** had reported similar sightings. Local fishermen witnessed something initially believed to be a seal or porpoise…

11. **ruse:** _____

In order to avenge the damage to his reputation, Wetherell came up with this **ruse** and fooled the entire world!

EXERCISE 2 / USING WORDS IN CONTEXT

Fill in the blank with the vocabulary word that best completes the sentence. In some cases, you may need to change the tense or form of a verb or the number of a noun.

conjecture	expound	elicit	credible	deleterious	deride
fabricate	populace	fortuitous	ruse	incongruous	

1. Tara and Mark's _____ encounter at a bus stop led to their dating and, later, getting married.

2. The rumor about the company closing didn't come from a(n) _____ source, so we didn't believe it.

3. Robert's friends had a clever _____ to keep him out of the house while they set up for his surprise party.

4. It seemed as if the entire _____ of the town gathered in the square to welcome back the soldiers.

5. The new class president _____ on the reasons the old school library should be remodeled.

6. The other players on the basketball team _____ Owen for missing easy shots that he should have made.

7. Rather than admit that she lost her phone, Michelle _____ a lie about how it was stolen from her car.

8. The bad joke Mr. Grudzina made in class _____ a loud groan from the students.

9. There is a lot of evidence showing that smoking is _____ to your health.

10. We made several _____ as to why Eliza missed the meeting, but they all turned out to be false.

11. Even though two people worked together on writing the book, there was nothing _____ about it, and all the chapters fit together perfectly.

EXERCISE 3 / READING COMPREHENSION AND ANALYSIS

Select the best answers to the following questions based on a close and thorough reading of " 'Nessie.' "

1. The best reason the writer opens the " 'Strange Spectacle on Loch Ness' " section by saying it is when the "more modern-day history" began is to

    A. show that proof of Nessie's existence has been around for a long time.

    B. place the first Nessie sighting in a greater historical context.

    C. indicate that there have been many recent sightings of Nessie.

    D. suggest that stories of Nessie have been around before 1933.

    E. conceal ignorance of the date the event actually took place.

2. Why would the *Inverness Courier* emphasize that one of the witnesses in the 1933 sighting was a " 'well-known businessman' "?

    A. to give a hint of the witness's identity

    B. to provide greater accuracy to the news story

    C. to suggest that the witness was a reliable source

    D. to indicate why the witness was at the loch

    E. to make a strange story seem more realistic

3. Which information from the passage is the most important element of Wetherell's deception?

    A. He convinced the public that Nessie exists.

    B. He tricked Wilson into photographing a toy submarine.

    C. He used a hippo foot to make fake tracks.

    D. He got the *Daily Mail* to print a fake photograph.

    E. He led the public to believe Nessie had been photographed.

4. Which of the following is a way that "Picts, Pictures, and Prayers" can be improved?

    A. explain how Nessie initially got into Loch Ness

    B. indicate what made St. Columba want to visit Loch Ness

    C. explore the Picts' other pagan superstitions

    D. explain when the Picts lived in Scotland and when the Romans invaded

    E. make a connection between the Picts' drawings and water-horses/water-kelpies

5. How is this passage organized?

    A. chronologically

    B. point and counterpoint

    C. cause and effect

    D. order of importance

    E. by topic

EXERCISE 4 / MAKING INFERENCES

Choose the best answer.

1. A person trying to make a **credible** argument would most likely use

    A. numerous graphs and images.

    B. a large amount of information.

    C. valid supporting details.

    D. opinions, not facts.

2. Which of the following is most likely to cause fans to **deride** a famous musician?

    A. claiming that he hates his fans

    B. always responding to fan mail

    C. never touring to support an album

    D. having an album reach platinum status

3. Which of the following situations could be considered **fortuitous**?

    A. a hurricane during a vacation at the beach

    B. having a dream of something that happens the next day

    C. receiving a perfect score on a test

    D. getting fired and offered a job on the same day

4. Which of the following could NOT be considered **incongruous**?

    A. two versions of a story that contradict each other

    B. making rude jokes at a formal business meeting

    C. bright Christmas decorations on someone's house

    D. an actor wearing shorts when portraying Abe Lincoln

5. What can be logically inferred by the writer's comment that Nessie could be "a remnant of the world that existed 65 million years ago"?

    A. Nessie could be a plesiosaur.

    B. Nessie is older than Loch Ness.

    C. Nessie did not die when the dinosaurs did.

    D. Nessie probably didn't survive the age of dinosaurs.

EXERCISE 5 / ROOTS, PREFIXES, AND SUFFIXES

Answer the questions below that are designed to help you arrive at some conclusions about word families and origins.

1. Briefly define **credible** in your own words. What part of speech is **credible**?

    _____

    _____

    A. You should already be familiar with the root and prefix that make up **credible**. Briefly explain in your own words how **credible** derives its meaning from these parts.

    _____

    _____

    _____

2. Briefly define **incongruous** in your own words. What part of speech is **incongruous**?

_____

A. Divide **incongruous** into its four syllables.

_____

_____

B. You should already be familiar with most of these syllables as word elements. List and briefly define the elements of **incongruous** that you already know.

_____

_____

_____

_____

C. Now consider the one-syllable/word element with which you are probably not familiar. What word associated with geometry shares this same element as **incongruous**? Define it in your own words.

_____

_____

_____

D. Given the meaning of **incongruous** and the related word, what does their common root most likely mean?

_____

_____

3. Briefly define **populace** in your own words. What part of speech is **populace**?

_____

A. You might already be familiar with the root of **populace**. List several words that are probably derived from this same root and define each in your own words.

_____

_____

_____

B. What does the root most likely mean?

_____

_____

JAPAN'S ATLANTIS

On an ordinary day in 1986, a resident of Japan's Yonaguni Island went on a scuba dive and made an unexpected and **serendipitous** discovery. There, right before his eyes, was what appeared to be ancient ruins. When marine geologist Masaaki Kimura, a professor at the University of the Ryukyus in Okinawa, Japan, was contacted, he investigated the site and agreed that they had uncovered a sunken underwater city—perhaps from a civilization that had disappeared thousands of years ago. There are several formal names for the location, such as the Yonaguni Monument, but it is **colloquially** known as "Japan's Atlantis" after its more famous Western counterpart.

But what exactly was found, and were the structures beneath the waves undoubtedly created by people? Or, were the unique rock formations simply the result of natural phenomena, such as ocean currents or **tectonic** activity among the earth's gigantic moving plates? There continues to be much debate on the issue.

What Is the Yonaguni Monument?

The Yonaguni Monument sits in the waters off the coast of Okinawa, 75 miles from the eastern coast of Taiwan. The entire site is roughly the size of three football fields and made almost entirely of sandstone. Many of the rocks have right angles, creating formations that look like stairs and other structures. Some have been described as temples, terraces, arches, roads, walkways, a pool, and even a sphinx that looks like an ancient king! Standing at roughly 886 ft. in height, the pyramid is the most amazing feature. Kimura and some other archaeologists think that it looks like the Mayan pyramids. More interestingly, there is a formation that, oddly enough, has a vague resemblance to a face. Were these structures built by human hands?

Humans Built Yonaguni

Determining whether the Yonaguni Monument was man-made relies on a few key questions. What, exactly, was also found at the site that indicates a human presence? What happened to the people who lived there? Are there any other explanations for the peculiar structures?

According to Kimura and some other archaeologists, stone tools and pottery were found on Yonaguni Island and other nearby islands, which suggests that people did live there at one point in time. They also **allege** that carvings and writings were found on the structures, as well as markings on the rocks that were made by tools, suggesting that the stones had originally been quarried. The straight sides of the stones are also of interest, especially since right angles and straight lines rarely occur in nature.

Who could have built the site if it is artificial, though? There have been many hypotheses. The most popular is that the Mu were responsible. While perhaps it is **dubious**, according to legend, the Mu were an ancient people who were technologically advanced compared to other civilizations at the time. They created the city, but it eventually fell into the sea. Why did it collapse? One theory is that sea levels rose, submerging a land bridge between Taiwan and Yonaguni. If this were the case, the monument would be approximately 10,000 years old. There is also the possibility that shifts in the earth's plates, leading to earthquakes and volcanos, caused the entire city to sink. The site would then be 5,000-6,000 years old. According to the story, after the city disappeared under the water, the survivors left and established other civilizations, most notably the Mayan. Is there any **veracity** to this interpretation, or is it based on speculation and **spurious** evidence?

Nature Made Yonaguni

Many geologists **refute** the idea that this formation is an ancient city. Robert Schoch, a professor of Natural Sciences at Boston University, is one of the most well known. He has dived the site and concluded that it occurred naturally.

Some scientists believe that there is no proof the Mu existed. They say that there are people who claim to be experts on the subject, but aren't credible because they seem to have an **affinity** for superstition rather than for history. Even if the Mu story is false, the tools and pottery found on the island probably came from small communities that would not have been capable of building monuments. Additionally, the statement that writing and images were present is untrue, according to Schoch. He believes they are actually natural scratches on the rock. As to the "face" that was found at the site, it could have been caused by erosion instead of being sculpted by humans.

What could have created the right angles and the stair-like structures? Geologists point to the characteristics of sandstone, the rocks that make up the monument. Sandstone, unlike many other rocks, splits in an unusual way: When **fissures** occur in sandstone, the rock breaks along straight lines. The amount of geological activity at the location (e.g., earthquakes and volcanos) could easily provide the force necessary to split sandstone. While the appearance of the rock may be unusual, the geologists state that it is perfectly understandable given the conditions at Yonaguni.

Researchers from many different fields, ranging from geology to archaeology, continue to study the Yonaguni Monument, hoping to ascertain exactly what it is. Is the scene beneath the water's surface the remains of an ancient city, or merely something that can be explained by natural forces? One thing is certain: A wonder lies beyond the Yonaguni coast, regardless if it is natural or man-made.

EXERCISE 1 / WORD LIST

Use the context in which the word is used to determine what the word probably means. Write a brief definition in the space provided.

1. **affinity:** _____

   Some scientists believe that there is no proof the Mu existed. They say that there are people who claim to be experts on the subject, but aren't credible because they seem to have an **affinity** for superstition rather than for history.

2. **allege:** _____

   They also **allege** that carvings and writings were found on the structures, as well as markings on the rocks that were made by tools, suggesting that the stones had originally been quarried.

3. **colloquial:** _____

   There are several formal names for the location, such as the Yonaguni Monument, but it is **colloquially** known as "Japan's Atlantis" after its more famous Western counterpart.

4. **dubious:** _____

   While perhaps it is **dubious**, according to legend, the Mu were an ancient people who were technologically advanced compared to other civilizations at the time.

5. **fissure:** _____

   Sandstone, unlike many other rocks, splits in an unusual way: When **fissures** occur in sandstone, the rock breaks along straight lines.

6. **refute:** _____

   Many geologists **refute** the idea that this formation is an ancient city. Robert Schoch, a professor of Natural Sciences at Boston University, is one of the most well known. He has dived the site and concluded that it occurred naturally.

7. **serendipitous:** _____

   On an ordinary day in 1986, a resident of Japan's Yonaguni Island went on a scuba dive and made an unexpected and **serendipitous** discovery. There, right before his eyes, was what appeared to be ancient ruins.

8. **spurious:** _____

Is there any veracity to this interpretation, or is it based on speculation and **spurious** evidence?

9. **tectonic:** _____

Or, were the unique rock formations simply the result of natural phenomena, such as ocean currents or **tectonic** activity among the earth's gigantic moving plates.

10. **veracity:** _____

Is there any **veracity** to this interpretation, or is it based on speculation and spurious evidence?

EXERCISE 2 / USING WORDS IN CONTEXT

Fill in the blank with the vocabulary word that best completes the sentence. In some cases, you may need to change the tense or form of a verb or the number of a noun.

fissure	allege	refute	spurious	serendipitous
affinity	veracity	colloquial	dubious	tectonic

1. Because all the evidence had been lost, nobody could check on the _____ of the defendant's testimony.

2. There was a large _____ in the sidewalk, and the roots of the oak tree were beginning to come through.

3. Lisa has a(n) _____ for large books and never reads any that have fewer than a thousand pages.

4. Dr. Johnson gave a lecture on the _____ theory that Percy Shelley wrote *Frankenstein*.

5. Scientists studying _____ believe that the seven continents once made up one supercontinent, called "Pangaea."

6. It was _____ that our vacation in the Bahamas happened right before the hurricane hit; we felt lucky.

7. Although Shae had taken Spanish classes for ten years, she couldn't understand the _____ phrases used on television.

8. The new law was founded on _____ statistics that were inaccurate and over twenty years old.

9. We couldn't _____ the hypothesis that monarch butterflies use the sun to navigate during their migration south.

10. Beth _____ that her brother threw the wild party at their house while their parents were away.

EXERCISE 3 / READING COMPREHENSION AND ANALYSIS

Select the best answers to the following questions based on a close and thorough reading of "Japan's Atlantis."

1. How are the most important aspects of the passage organized?

    A. chronologically

    B. point and counterpoint

    C. cause and effect

    D. order of importance

    E. by topic

2. Why is it relevant that the pyramid of Yonaguni "looks like the Mayan pyramids"?

    A. It indicates that the monument was undeniably a land bridge.

    B. It supports the idea that sandstone breaks along planes.

    C. It proves that the Yonaguni Monument was man-made.

    D. It proves the Yonaguni Monument was built by the Maya.

    E. It suggests that the Yonaguni Monument may have been built by the Mu.

3. Which is NOT an argument made by geologists that Yonaguni is a natural phenomenon?

    A. Characteristics of sandstone explain the formations.

    B. There is no evidence that the Mu existed.

    C. Small communities could not have built a monument.

    D. Kimura is an unreliable source of information.

    E. Tectonic activity would cause the rocks to split.

4. Re-read the following excerpt from the third paragraph of "Nature Made Yonaguni."

> "Sandstone, unlike many other rocks, splits in an unusual way: When fissures occur in sandstone, the rock breaks along straight lines. The amount of geological activity at the location (e.g., earthquakes and volcanos) could easily provide the force necessary to split sandstone. While the appearance of the rock may be unusual, the geologists state that it is perfectly understandable given the conditions at Yonaguni."

The word *conditions* refers to

A. cracks in rocks.

B. the land bridge.

C. tectonic movement.

D. the age of the monument.

E. the softness of sandstone.

5. With which of the following statements would the writer most likely agree?

A. The evidence clearly indicates that the Mu built the monument.

B. Tectonic activity and the characteristics of sandstone are responsible for the monument.

C. No one will ever know whether or not Yonaguni is man-made.

D. The structure was natural, but later modified by humans.

E. There may be other theories explaining what the Yonaguni Monument is.

EXERCISE 4 / MAKING INFERENCES

Choose the best answer.

1. Someone who has an **affinity** for snow would probably
   A. learn to ski.
   B. travel frequently.
   C. live in Florida.
   D. drive a truck.

2. If someone makes a **dubious** comment, others would be most likely to
   A. develop a great respect for the person.
   B. spread the information to other people.
   C. attempt to find out if it's true.
   D. never think about it again.

3. Which of the following situations would be considered **serendipitous**?
   A. getting sunburned after refusing to use sunscreen
   B. overhearing someone talking about you
   C. running into a friend you haven't seen since kindergarten
   D. getting a role in a school play after having a great audition

4. Which of the following would have the greatest **veracity**?
   A. a good guess
   B. an urban legend
   C. a conspiracy theory
   D. an article in a newspaper

5. Re-read the entire first paragraph. Which of the following is NOT a logical inference that can be made from it?
   A. Atlantis is believed to be an underwater city.
   B. Yonaguni Island is considered "Eastern."
   C. The diver was not a marine geologist.
   D. The diver contacted Masaaki Kimura.

EXERCISE 5 / ROOTS, PREFIXES, AND SUFFIXES

Answer the questions below that are designed to help you arrive at some conclusions about word families and origins.

1. Briefly define **colloquial** in your own words. What part of speech is **colloquial**?

   _____

   A. Divide the word into its three most likely elements or components (not syllables).

      _____

      _____

   B. Consider the following words, all of which are based on a form of the same root as **colloquial**. Briefly define each in your own words. Feel free to consult a dictionary or other source that explains word history in its definitions.

      elocution:

      _____

      _____

      eloquence:

      _____

      _____

      soliloquy:

      _____

      _____

      ventriloquism:

      _____

      _____

      What meaning do these four words have in common? What does their shared root most likely mean?

      _____

      _____

   C. What is the meaning or function of the word's final element? List a few examples of other words that use this suffix to serve this purpose.

      _____

      _____

      _____

      _____

D. Look at the following words, all of which use the same prefix as **colloquial**. Briefly define each in your own words. Feel free to consult a dictionary or other source that explains word history in its definitions.

collusion:

_____

_____

collection:

_____

_____

collateral:

_____

_____

colleague:

_____

_____

What meaning do all of these words have in common? What does their shared prefix most likely mean?

_____

_____

E. Briefly explain in your own words how **colloquial** derives its meaning from is parts.

_____

_____

_____

_____

_____

2. Briefly define **veracity** in your own words. What part of speech is **veracity**?

_____

A. Divide the word into its two most likely elements or components (not syllables).

_____

_____

B. List some other words that probably contain the first component of **veracity**. Define each in your own words.

_____

_____

_____

_____

C. You should already be familiar with this word element. What does it mean?

_____

_____

_____

_____

D. List some other words that probably contain the second component of **veracity**. Define each in your own words.

_____

_____

_____

_____

E. What are the function and meaning of this component?

_____

_____

_____

_____

F. Briefly explain in your own words how **veracity** derives its meaning from its parts.

_____

_____

_____

_____

WHERE IS AMELIA EARHART?

At 7:42 a.m. on July 2, 1937, the *Itasca*, a US Coast Guard ship, received a distress call over its radio:

"We must be on you, but we cannot see you," the female pilot said. "Fuel is running low. Been unable to reach you by radio. We are flying at 1,000 feet."

Time was crucial. The airplane was scheduled to refuel on Howland Island, but had gotten lost along the way.

The crew of the *Itasca* struggled to contact the pilot, but all their efforts were in vain. They couldn't get through! The pilot would have to navigate her way unaided through the thick clouds—and she had to do it quickly.

For the next hour, the ship made more unsuccessful attempts to reach the blind aircraft. Then, a second radio transmission came through:

"We are on the line 157 337. We will repeat this message. We will repeat this on 6210 kilocycles. Wait."

No other message followed. It would be the last time anyone would hear from Amelia Earhart. Just when they had nearly finished their flight around the world, she, her navigator, Fred Noonan, and her Lockheed Electra plane, vanished without a trace, leading to one of the greatest mysteries in American history.

If you were to ask back then, "Who would be brave enough to attempt a flight **circumnavigating** the globe?" the answer would certainly be "Amelia Earhart." Earhart was an expert pilot with an **insatiable** passion for aviation that began in young adulthood. Her interest in aeronautics was first sparked in 1916. While she was working as a nurse for the Red Cross in Toronto, Amelia spent much of her free time watching the Royal Flying Corps training, completely enraptured by their skillful movements. Her first opportunity to actually *ride* in a plane, however, came in 1920 when she took an hour-long flight at the Long Beach Air Show in California. Both experiences made one thing clear: Earhart would not be kept on the ground. One day, she would soar through the sky in a plane of her own.

She was determined. Earhart learned how to fly, bought her first airplane, and earned her flying license, all in 1921. It was obvious that she had the heart of an adventurer, combined with an unstoppable ambition. She wouldn't be content, though, with being just a good pilot—she had to be the best. She began setting records at an astonishing rate. The following are just a few:

First woman to fly above 14,000 feet (October 1922)

First woman to fly across the Atlantic Ocean (June 1928)

First woman to fly *solo* across the Atlantic (May 1932)

First woman to fly from the West Coast to the East Coast (August 1932)

Earhart was also the **recipient** of several **prestigious** awards, including the National Geographic Society's Gold Medal, the Distinguished Flying Cross, and the Cross of the Knight of the Legion of Honor. She certainly had an enormous amount of experience, and it was clear that she was an adept pilot.

Earhart had already become a famous pilot when she set her sights on something even greater. She wanted to be the first woman to fly around the world. Her extraordinary plan was to leave from Miami, Florida, on June, 1, 1937, then fly sequentially to Brazil, Africa, India, Indonesia, Australia, Papua New Guinea, and finally to

California. Everything seemed to be in order—but then, a series of unlucky circumstances led to tragedy.

The largest part of the journey proved to be relatively easy and uneventful; Earhart and Noonan flew 22,000 miles and had only 7,000 left to go when they landed in Papua New Guinea to refuel and make minor repairs. Earhart's next stop should have been Howland Island, a small piece of land roughly a mile-and-a-half long and a half-mile wide. The island would be difficult to locate from the sky, even on a clear day, but the weather on July 2nd was not in Earhart's favor and was becoming a serious **impediment** to navigation. The area was overcast, with poor visibility, so Earhart couldn't locate the island or the *Itasca*. She had to rely on other devices to find her way, and, unfortunately, they may have all been unreliable or absent. The maps that she had with her, for example, might have been off by several miles. Furthermore, to make room for extra fuel, some of her radio equipment was left behind—if it hadn't been, it could possibly have saved her life.

The United States government searched for Earhart for roughly six months; the Supreme Court of Los Angeles declared her legally dead on January 5, 1939. The official government report states that she crashed into the Pacific Ocean after her fuel was **depleted**.

However, there is an alternate story.

Three hundred fifty miles from Howland Island is Nikumaroro Island, which is uninhabited and has few visitors. It's possible that Earhart and her navigator didn't crash into the ocean, but became stranded on Nikumaroro, instead. A **meticulous** search of the island yielded evidence of castaways, including campsites with improvised tools and leftover scraps of food. Other expeditions years later uncovered additional artifacts like scrap metal and Plexiglas (both, perhaps, from an airplane) and a woman's cosmetics jar. The strongest evidence, however, may be the partial remains of a skeleton.

In 1940, the bones were recovered and analyzed by a doctor, who ultimately concluded that they were from a middle-aged man, not Earhart. But modern research suggests that the original results could have been wrong. After all, **forensic** technology was not as precise then as it is today. Perhaps the bones belonged to Earhart—or perhaps not. New evidence and theories about where Earhart died does turn up infrequently, but nothing **irrefutable** enough to finally close the case.

The search continues. Will the complex puzzle involving one of the world's **eminent** aviators ever be solved? Will we ever know if the plane was lost in the Pacific Ocean, or if it landed on Nikumaroro? Those questions may never be answered, leaving Amelia Earhart's disappearance as one of the world's greatest **conundrums**.

EXERCISE 1 / WORD LIST

Use the context in which the word is used to determine what the word probably means. Write a brief definition in the space provided.

1. **circumnavigate:** _____

   If you were to ask back then, "Who would be brave enough to attempt a flight **circumnavigating** the globe?" the answer would certainly be "Amelia Earhart."

2. **conundrum:** _____

   Those questions may never be answered, leaving Amelia Earhart's disappearance as one of the world's greatest **conundrums**.

3. **deplete:** _____

   The official government report states that she crashed into the Pacific Ocean after her fuel was **depleted**.

4. **eminent:** _____

   Will the complex puzzle involving one of the world's **eminent** aviators ever be solved?

5. **forensic:** _____

   In 1940, the bones were recovered and analyzed by a doctor, who ultimately concluded that they were from a middle-aged man, not Earhart. But modern research suggests that the original results could have been wrong. After all, **forensic** technology was not as precise then as it is today. Perhaps the bones belonged to Earhart—or perhaps not.

6. **impediment:** _____

   The island would be difficult to locate from the sky, even on a clear day, but the weather on July 2nd was not in Earhart's favor and was becoming a serious **impediment** to navigation.

7. **insatiable:** _____

   Earhart was an expert pilot with an **insatiable** passion for aviation that began in young adulthood.

8. **irrefutable:** _____

   New evidence and theories about where Earhart died does turn up infrequently, but nothing **irrefutable** enough to finally close the case.

9. **meticulous:** _____

A **meticulous** search of the island yielded evidence of castaways, including campsites with improvised tools and leftover scraps of food.

10. **prestigious:** _____

Earhart was also the recipient of several **prestigious** awards, including the National Geographic Society's Gold Medal, the Distinguished Flying Cross, and the Cross of the Knight of the Legion of Honor.

11. **recipient:** _____

Earhart was also the **recipient** of several prestigious awards, including the National Geographic Society's Gold Medal, the Distinguished Flying Cross, and the Cross of the Knight of the Legion of Honor.

EXERCISE 2 / USING WORDS IN CONTEXT

Fill in the blank with the vocabulary word that best completes the sentence. In some cases, you may need to change the tense or form of a verb or the number of a noun.

prestigious	meticulous	eminent	irrefutable	forensic	circumnavigate
deplete	recipient	impediment	insatiable	conundrum	

1. René Descartes was a(n) _____ philosopher who originated the phrase "I think, therefore, I am."

2. Ben _____ his entire savings at the electronics store when he bought new computer parts.

3. Contrary to popular belief, Ferdinand Magellan was not the first person to _____ the globe by ship.

4. Jenna's _____ attention to detail enabled her to become an excellent editor and proofreader.

5. A speech _____ made Kayla uncomfortable reading aloud, but her classmates helped boost her confidence.

6. In 1993, Toni Morrison had the honor of receiving the _____ Nobel Prize in Literature.

7. The reporters thought the photograph was _____ proof that the Loch Ness Monster existed, but later, they found out that the picture was a fake.

8. Alexander the Great's _____ ambition led him to conquer the Persian Empire and take over many countries in the Mediterranean.

9. Mark was faced with a(n) _____: How could he be on the debate team and in drama club if the meetings were at the same time?

10. A careful analysis of _____ evidence suggested that the suspect was not the culprit.

11. Because Joe never missed class, he was the _____ of the Perfect Attendance Award.

EXERCISE 3 / READING COMPREHENSION AND ANALYSIS

Select the best answers to the following questions based on a close and thorough reading of "Where Is Amelia Earhart?"

1. What is the most likely reason the author begins the passage with dialogue between Earhart and the *Itasca*?

    A. to present Earhart's last words to the reader

    B. to show that Earhart's disappearance was mysterious

    C. to create suspense about Earhart's disappearance

    D. to convey the idea that Earhart was a poor pilot

    E. to show that Earhart and Noonan were lost

2. In the paragraph beginning, "She was determined," the phrase "all in 1921" conveys the same thought as which of the following?

    A. "She was determined"

    B. "heart of an adventurer"

    C. "being just a good pilot"

    D. "bought her first airplane"

    E. "began setting records"

3. In the paragraph that begins, "Earhart was also the recipient," what is the relevance of the remark that Earhart had "an enormous amount of experience"?

    A. It supports the idea that Earhart was ambitious.

    B. It stresses the practice and skill people need to become a pilot.

    C. It indicates that not many people won awards for flying.

    D. It makes her disappearance more peculiar.

    E. It foreshadows the tragedy that would happen.

4. Which of the following would REFUTE a statement made in the passage?

    A. Earhart had an accident before beginning her around-the-world flight.

    B. At the time of the accident, Nikumaroro Island was called Gardner Island.

    C. Earhart was the first person to fly from Hawaii to the US mainland.

    D. The *Itasca* received a third transmission from Earhart.

    E. The conclusion of the bone study is debated by other scientists.

5. Which would be the best alternative title for the passage?

    A. The Mystery of Amelia Earhart's Last Flight

    B. Amelia Earhart: Famous Female Aviator

    C. Another Disappearance over the Pacific Ocean

    D. Riddle of Earhart's Disappearance Finally Solved

    E. The Many Accomplishments of Amelia Earhart

EXERCISE 4 / MAKING INFERENCES

Choose the best answer.

1. Which of the following is an example of something being **depleted**?

    A. a pencil that becomes shorter after sharpening

    B. an ice cube melting in the sun

    C. the volume of music being lowered

    D. the decreasing battery life of a laptop

2. Which sentence shows the best use of the word **prestigious**?

    A. The GPS gave us prestigious directions on our way to the cabin.

    B. Al Capone was one of the most prestigious gangsters in American History.

    C. The most prestigious university in the country hires the best professors.

    D. The most prestigious task on my to-do list is to study for my exam.

3. Someone with an **insatiable** love of skiing should

    A. also enjoy ice skating and hockey.

    B. limit skiing to only once a month.

    C. have a season pass to one of the ski slopes.

    D. record and watch the Winter Olympics.

4. If Harry were presented with a **conundrum**, he would be least likely to

    A. search for possible solutions.

    B. look up additional information.

    C. ask others for information and advice.

    D. solve the problem quickly.

5. The best example of a **meticulous** doctor is one who

    A. researches other fields of medicine.

    B. schedules many appointments.

    C. analyzes lab results carefully.

    D. stays at work after hours.

EXERCISE 5 / ROOTS, PREFIXES, AND SUFFIXES

Answer the questions below that are designed to help you arrive at some conclusions about word families and origins.

1. Briefly define **circumnavigate** in your own words. What part of speech is **circumnavigate**?

    _____

    _____

    A. Divide the word into its two most likely roots.

        _____

    B. List some words that probably share the first root with **circumnavigate**. What does this root most likely mean?

        _____

        _____

        _____

C. You know that the second portion of the word, *navigate*, has to do with travel, especially leading or guiding the traveler on the right track. Put the two parts and their meanings together. What does the word **circumnavigate** *literally* mean?

_____

_____

_____

2. Briefly define **impediment** in your own words. What part of speech is **impediment**?

_____

A. Divide the word into its three most likely elements or components (not syllables).

_____

_____

B. You should already be familiar with the word's first element. What is it and what does it mean? List a few words that begin with this same element.

_____

_____

_____

C. Consider the following words, all of which are based on a form of the same root as **impediment**. This root, *pedi*, comes from Latin and means "to shackle the feet." Briefly define each in your own words. Feel free to consult a dictionary or other source that explains word history in its definitions, but do not merely copy the information verbatim from the source.

pedal:

_____

_____

pedestrian:

_____

_____

pedicure:

_____

_____

What meaning do all of these words have in common?

_____

_____

D. Consider the following words, all of which use the same suffix as **impediment**. Briefly define each in your own words. Feel free to consult a dictionary or other source that explains word history in its definitions, but do not merely copy the information verbatim from the source.

amazement:

_____

_____

merriment:

_____

_____

payment:

_____

_____

requirement:

_____

_____

What meaning do all of these words have in common? What function does their shared suffix most likely perform?

_____

_____

_____

E. Put the three elements and their meanings together. What does the word **impediment** *literally* mean? How might it derive its current usage from this literal meaning?

_____

_____

_____

_____

_____

THE AMAZING NEUTRINO

As most people know, our universe began about fourteen billion years ago with what is called the "Big Bang." *Everything* that exists today had been contained in a space smaller than an electron, but in an instant, it became unstable and blew apart with incredible force. What most people *don't* know, though, is that the enormous explosion also created exceptionally unusual subatomic particles. These continue to **diffuse** throughout the universe. One of the oddest of these particles is called the *neutrino*. What makes this one thing so weird?

First of all, neutrinos are copious; they are one of the most abundant particles in the universe, yet they have almost no mass. Mass is essentially the same as weight, with no consideration of size. Therefore, if a bowling ball and a basketball are the same exact size, the bowling ball has more mass because it is heavier. In fact, neutrinos are so incredibly small and weigh such a tiny amount that their mass is **indeterminate**. They are 2,000 times smaller than an electron. And an electron is **minuscule**, only about twenty-five *trillionths* (2.5×10^{-11}) of an inch in diameter.

Another problem that makes understanding neutrinos even more complicated is that they travel at nearly the speed of light, and it is difficult to learn much about them because of how fast they move. Neutrinos were not even proven to exist until 1956, although the possibility that they were real had been postulated earlier. The scientists who discovered the neutrino won the Nobel Prize in Physics, but not until 1995. That delay was probably because the complexity of the neutrino made it difficult to understand. However, we now know **substantively** more about them.

For example, physicists in the 21st century know that neutrinos are being created every second, even after the Big Bang. They come into existence through the decay of radioactive elements. Physicists estimate that the universe contains 1.2×10^{89} neutrinos (that's 12 followed by 89 zeroes), which is an **incomprehensibly** large number. They emanate from nuclear power plants, from nuclear explosions, from our sun, and from the deaths of stars, particularly those that turn into supernovas. Since the discovery of neutrinos, scientists have built detectors that try to "capture" neutrinos. However, capturing a neutrino is not like capturing a lion and putting it in a cage: A neutrino is captured when it strikes an electron, and the **interaction** causes an electrical charge to be emitted. You may ask, "If electrons and neutrinos are so small, how could they ever collide with one another?" The answer is that collisions *do* happen, but they are extremely rare.

Neutrino detectors all over the world have attempted to provide proof of these subatomic crashes. One detector is in a huge 50,000-ton (approximately 12,000,000-gallon) vat of water in Japan. Another is embedded in a cubic kilometer-sized block of ice at the South Pole. A third detector is under construction a mile deep in an abandoned gold mine in South Dakota.

These gigantic collectors are hugely expensive, each one costing approximately a billion dollars. The number of detectors and their cost are clearly **indicative** of how important the study of neutrinos is. These devices have hundreds or thousands of photographic tubes in them to capture the flash that occurs when a neutrino hits an electron. Yet only a few thousand have ever been detected, despite their enormous number and the massive effort to locate them. Researchers at the South Pole detector counted only 28 neutrinos in its first two years of operation.

Why even try to analyze neutrinos? The answer to that question is simple: Neutrinos are all around us. The information about them is **invaluable** because studying simple particles allows researchers to grasp the properties of more mysterious objects. In other words, scientists cannot understand atoms without recognizing what they are made of. All atoms are made up of protons, neutrons, electrons, and other particles, like neutrinos. Not understanding what **constitutes** the atom is like not being able to do algebra if you can't do addition.

If neutrinos are **ubiquitous**, flying everywhere in the universe, why are human beings not being hit by them? Physicists and astronomers understand that neutrinos can and do travel completely through the earth, the sun, the emptiness of outer space, or anything else and only extremely rarely does one encounter something that impedes its movement. We are being bombarded by neutrinos constantly. In the one second that it took you to read "neutrinos constantly," approximately 600 *trillion* neutrinos passed through your body. Did you notice any of them? Of course not. They rarely interact with anything. It is estimated that if you captured every single neutrino that has passed through each human being that ever lived and weighed them, the total mass of the neutrinos would amount to fifteen-hundredths of one gram!

EXERCISE 1 / WORD LIST

Use the context in which the word is used to determine what the word probably means. Write a brief definition in the space provided.

1. **constitute:** _____

   All atoms are made up of protons, neutrons, electrons, and other particles, like neutrinos. Not understanding what **constitutes** the atom is like not being able to do algebra if you can't do addition.

2. **diffuse:** _____

   What most people *don't* know, though, is that the enormous explosion also created exceptionally unusual subatomic particles. These continue to **diffuse** throughout the universe.

3. **incomprehensible:** _____

   Physicists estimate that the universe contains 1.2×10^{89} neutrinos (that's 12 followed by 89 zeroes), which is an **incomprehensibly** large number.

4. **indeterminate:** _____

   In fact, neutrinos are so incredibly small and weigh such a tiny amount that their mass is **indeterminate**.

5. **indicative:** _____

   The number of detectors and their cost are clearly **indicative** of how important the study of neutrinos is.

6. **interaction:** _____

   A neutrino is captured when it strikes an electron, and the **interaction** causes an electrical charge to be emitted.

7. **invaluable:** _____

   The information about them is **invaluable** because studying simple particles allows researchers to grasp the properties of more mysterious objects.

8. **minuscule:** _____

   And an electron is **minuscule**, only about twenty-five *trillionths* (2.5×10^{-11}) of an inch in diameter.

9. **substantive:** _____

   That delay was probably because the complexity of the neutrino made it difficult to understand. However, we now know **substantively** more about them.

10. **ubiquitous:** _____

   If neutrinos are **ubiquitous**, flying everywhere in the universe, why are human beings not being hit by them?

EXERCISE 2 / USING WORDS IN CONTEXT

Fill in the blank with the vocabulary word that best completes the sentence. In some cases, you may need to change the tense or form of a verb or the number of a noun.

ubiquitous	invaluable	constitute	interaction	indeterminate
substantive	indicative	diffuse	minuscule	incomprehensible

1. Kayla teased Joey for complaining about his _____ problems when things like famine, disease, and world hunger exist.

2. A book on neuroscience would probably be _____ to someone who has never studied biology.

3. When we turned the heater on in the middle of winter, it took several minutes before the warm air _____ throughout the room.

4. My father's advice about cars was _____, considering that he had been a mechanic for thirty years.

5. The salesperson claimed that the new device would be _____: Every person in the world would eventually own one.

6. Several short stories _____ *The Decameron*, a book written by Giovanni Boccaccio in the 14th century.

7. Because we didn't have an appointment, we knew we would have to wait a(n) _____ amount of time to see the doctor.

8. The improper _____ that happened yesterday led to the two employees getting fired for giving away company secrets to a competitor.

9. Amelia Earhart's numerous achievements were _____ of a brave woman who would never give up.

10. The three archaeologists had _____ knowledge of ancient civilizations and claimed that the Mu people never existed.

EXERCISE 3 / READING COMPREHENSION AND ANALYSIS

Select the best answers to the following questions based on a close and thorough reading of "The Amazing Neutrino."

1. Which list of facts accurately represents the information in the first two paragraphs?

    A. The mass of a neutrino cannot be determined; they travel faster than light; and they came into existence shortly after the Big Bang.

    B. Neutrinos were discovered prior to 1950; they are difficult to study; and bowling balls and basketballs have different masses.

    C. Mass is essentially the same as weight; neutrinos are an extremely common particle; and the Big Bang occurred approximately fourteen billion years ago.

    D. The neutrino has existed since only the 1950s; the universe contains an enormous number of neutrinos; and neutrinos travel at close to the speed of light.

    E. Bowling balls weigh more than basketballs; studying neutrinos is difficult because of their speed; and neutrinos are not much smaller than electrons.

2. Which, according to the passage, is NOT a reason that neutrinos are difficult to study?

    A. There are too many of them.

    B. They are small and have little mass.

    C. They can be detected only if they hit electrons.

    D. Neutrino detectors cost around a billion dollars.

    E. They can pass through most objects undetected.

3. Why did the author include the information that the "South Pole detector counted only 28 neutrinos" immediately after writing that "only a few thousand have ever been detected"?

    A. The author wanted to prove that the detector at the South Pole was more efficient at detecting neutrinos.

    B. The author wanted to restate the point that the temperature at the South Pole helped scientists collect the neutrinos.

    C. The author wanted to stress that neutrinos can be detected with the proper equipment, if there is enough time.

    D. The author wanted to state the fact that the number of neutrinos detected is much smaller than the total number of neutrinos that exist.

    E. The author wanted to emphasize the point that detection of neutrinos is extremely difficult.

4. What is the best way to improve the passage?

    A. include more scientific facts about neutrinos

    B. name the scientists who won the Nobel Prize

    C. explain how neutrinos are similar to other subatomic particles

    D. list all the neutrino detectors in operation

    E. add a conclusion to sum up the passage

5. Why does the writer say that 1.2×10^{89} neutrinos is "12 followed by 89 zeroes"?

    A. to compare the number to that of atoms in the universe

    B. to make certain the reader understands the unique notation

    C. to emphasize the number of neutrinos in the universe

    D. to illustrate how small the neutrino actually is

    E. to show how many neutrinos are created by nuclear explosions

EXERCISE 4 / MAKING INFERENCES

Choose the best answer.

1. Which of the following things would be considered **indeterminate**?

    A. the number of undiscovered species

    B. the temperature at the equator

    C. the amount of money in your pocket

    D. the number of bones in the human body

2. Which of the following is the correct use of the word **indicative**?

    A. Animals in the fable are indicative of personality traits.

    B. The dead grass and withered plants were indicative of a drought.

    C. Lisa's dress was indicative of one that I wore last week.

    D. Tyler's absence was indicative of his involvement in the fight.

3. Which of the following is NOT an example of something being **diffused**?

    A. trains leaving stations in different directions

    B. particles of dust moving through the air

    C. heat being emitted from a fireplace

    D. pollen floating in the breeze

4. Which of the following is the best example of something that is **ubiquitous**?

    A. leaves on an old tree

    B. the reverence for life

    C. a song that plays during a movie

    D. umbrellas on a crowded beach

5. What can you infer is the reason the writer mentions sports equipment, lions in cages, and algebra?

    A. to put complicated ideas into simple terms

    B. to put scientific words into everyday language

    C. to create some humor in the passage

    D. to emphasize that knowing math is important in physics

EXERCISE 5 / ROOTS, PREFIXES, AND SUFFIXES

Answer the questions below that are designed to help you arrive at some conclusions about word families and origins.

1. Define **incomprehensible** in your own words. What part of speech is **incomprehensible**?

    _____

    A. Divide the word into its five most likely elements or components (not syllables).

    _____

    _____

    B. You are probably already familiar with all but one of these elements, the root. Write the meaning of each prefix and suffix listed above that you already know.

    _____

    _____

    _____

    _____

C. What is the most likely root of **incomprehensible**?

_____

D. Consider the following words, all of which are based on a form of the same root as **incomprehensible**. Briefly define each in your own words. Feel free to consult a dictionary or other source that explains word history in its definitions, but do not merely copy the information verbatim from the source.

apprehend:

_____

apprehensive:

_____

comprehend:

_____

comprehension:

_____

comprehensive:

_____

What meaning do all of these words have in common? What does their shared root most likely mean?

_____

_____

_____

2. Define **interaction** in your own words. What part of speech is **interaction**?

_____

A. Divide the word into its three elements or components.

_____

B. You are probably already familiar with all of these elements. List some other words that share the first element. Define each of these in your own words. What does this element mean?

_____

_____

_____

_____

_____

_____

C. List some other words that share the root. Define each of these in your own words. What does this root mean?

_____

_____

_____

_____

D. What is the function of the final element, the suffix? Provide a few examples.

_____

_____

_____

_____

E. Put the elements and their meanings together. What does the word **interaction** *literally* mean?

_____

_____

_____

_____

ROANOKE, THE LOST COLONY

In 1590, Governor John White, who had been appointed by Sir Walter Raleigh to organize a settlement in Virginia three years earlier, disembarked from his ship at Roanoke, an English colony in what is now the Outer Banks, North Carolina. Expecting to be greeted by his wife, daughter, or granddaughter—or *any* of the 118 settlers—he found the colony completely abandoned. Not a single person could be found, and there was no sign of what happened or where they went. The settlement was **devoid** of clues with the exception of two: the word "Croatoan" carved on a wooden post and "CRO" on a tree. What did the strange words **denote**, and what truly happened to the colony?

White's expedition to Roanoke was actually the last of three, and the previous one ended disastrously. The first trip, in 1584, was merely to explore and scout the island, and the second, in 1585, was to construct a fort. Soldiers, scientists, and miners settled there, but encountered numerous **insuperable** difficulties: They struggled to survive on their scant resources, and perhaps even worse, their crops failed. Additionally, arguments with the local tribes led to a series of bloody **altercations**, resulting in the murder of a Native American chief. It didn't take long for the soldiers to realize that the mission was a failure, and they returned home to England.

Based on this history, it should have seemed obvious that it would be extremely difficult, if not impossible, to establish a viable colony in Roanoke, yet the English tried again. The third expedition, in 1587, brought civilians—including women and children—to the settlement. The new immigrants were **cognizant** of the difficulties, but were hopeful, despite being fully aware that **precarious** conditions—hostile Native Americans and poor weather and soil—awaited them when they landed. However, they encountered the same problems as the previous colonists. They had insufficient resources to survive; White was forced to leave his family behind, and he returned to England for additional supplies.

Back in Europe, though, a war between Britain and the Spanish (the Anglo-Spanish War, 1585-1604) had reached its climax. Queen Elizabeth I forbid all ships from leaving the country, forcing them, instead, to defend England against the Spanish Armada. Unfortunately, during the time White was detained, something inexplicable was happening in Roanoke that would puzzle historians for centuries.

What occurred in Roanoke while White was away? Some historians suggest that a contagious disease unique to the New World swept through the settlement and killed all the settlers. It is also possible the Anglo-Spanish War spilled over to Roanoke, which was small, relatively unprotected, and susceptible to attack. Yet, no remains were found, and there were no signs of violence, making these two theories improbable. Did the settlers get desperate waiting for White and set out for England on their own, only to be lost at sea? It wouldn't be unlikely. Or were they captured and killed by Native Americans—a reasonable explanation, considering the **contentious** relationship between the two groups?

The theory that most historians accept would surprise you. They believe that the settlers were not harmed by the natives, but rather, **assimilated** into their culture and joined their tribes. The greatest pieces of evidence are the words "CRO" and "Croatoan" found at the colony and a hidden mark on a map painted by White himself.

Croatoan—now called Hatteras Island—is an island southeast of Roanoke. The tribe that lived there, called the Croatoans, could have pitied the desperate English and tried to help them. It may seem unbelievable, yet artifacts found at the site support this idea. At the site, archaeologists uncovered what looked to be part of a 16th-century gold signet ring with an image of a lion. Presumably, it belonged to a member of the wealthy and influential Kendall family. Scientists also found a writing tablet and part of a rapier, both of which are European in origin. Is it possible that these items belonged to the colonists, who left Roanoke, lived **amicably** among the tribe, and avoided conflicts?

The map created by White may indicate a second possibility. In 2012, the British Museum discovered a red and blue star concealed under a patch on the map; it was northwest of Roanoke, near the Albemarle Sound. Why White chose to conceal this spot is unknown. Some archaeologists have **postulated** that it marks the place the settlers went after leaving Roanoke, and

they began digging at the site, which they call "Site X." There, they discovered a particular kind of pottery called "Border ware," food storage jars, and parts of guns. The results offer the possibility of two additional theories of what happened to the colonists, suggesting that they either went to Site X or split into two groups and went there *and* to Croatoan.

What happened at Roanoke remains a wonder that, even in the 21st century, would be unusual and shocking. How could an entire community of 118 settlers vanish without a trace? Could the people have met a deadly end, or, to the contrary, started new lives in a new location, adopted by a group of benevolent natives? Research may reveal the answer one day—or perhaps, the puzzle will never be solved.

EXERCISE 1 / WORD LIST

Use the context in which the word is used to determine what the word probably means. Write a brief definition in the space provided.

1. **altercation:** _____

   Additionally, arguments with the local tribes led to a series of bloody **altercations**, resulting in the murder of a Native American chief.

2. **amicable:** _____

   Is it possible that these items belonged to the colonists, who left Roanoke, lived **amicably** among the tribe, and avoided conflicts?

3. **assimilate:** _____

   The theory that most historians accept would surprise you. They believe that the settlers were not harmed by the natives, but rather, **assimilated** into their culture and joined their tribes.

4. **cognizant:** _____

   The new immigrants were **cognizant** of the difficulties, but were hopeful, despite being fully aware that precarious conditions—hostile Native Americans and poor weather and soil—awaited them when they landed.

5. **contentious:** _____

   Or were they captured and killed by Native Americans—a reasonable explanation, considering the **contentious** relationship between the two groups?

6. **denote:** _____

   The settlement was devoid of clues with the exception of two: the word "Croatoan" carved on a wooden post and "CRO" on a tree. What did the strange words **denote**, and what truly happened to the colony?

7. **devoid:** _____

   The settlement was **devoid** of clues with the exception of two: the word "Croatoan" carved on a wooden post and "CRO" on a tree. What did the strange words denote, and what truly happened to the colony?

8. **insuperable:** _____

   Soldiers, scientists, and miners settled there, but encountered numerous **insuperable** difficulties: They struggled to survive on their scant resources, and perhaps even worse, their crops failed.

9. **postulate:** _____

   Why White chose to conceal this spot is unknown. Some archaeologists have **postulated** that it marks the place the settlers went after leaving Roanoke, and they began digging at the site, which they call "Site X."

10. **precarious:** _____

   The new immigrants were cognizant of the difficulties, but were hopeful, despite being fully aware that **precarious** conditions—hostile Native Americans and poor weather and soil— awaited them when they landed.

EXERCISE 2 / USING WORDS IN CONTEXT

Fill in the blank with the vocabulary word that best completes the sentence. In some cases, you may need to change the tense or form of a verb or the number of a noun.

postulate	cognizant	devoid	denote	altercation
contentious	assimilate	amicable	precarious	insuperable

1. The car accident was the cause of a serious _____ between the two drivers, which resulted in both of them being arrested.

2. When they studied old documents, the historians became _____ that the family had not been involved in the Civil War.

3. The unique handwriting on the manuscript _____ that it was written by Ernest Hemingway himself.

4. Mia discovered that her fear of heights was a(n) _____ obstacle in her desire to become a pilot.

5. The _____ relationship between the two basketball teams demonstrated excellent sportsmanship.

6. Liam is in a(n) _____ financial situation because he doesn't know if he'll be able to pay his rent this month.

7. The _____ relationship between the two actors prevented them from giving interviews together.

8. The immigrants who came to the United States had to quickly _____ to the American way of life.

9. The host of the television program foolishly _____ that the Pyramids of Giza were created by aliens.

10. The politician's platform was _____ of facts and statistics, so the voters were unlikely to give him their support.

EXERCISE 3 / READING COMPREHENSION AND ANALYSIS

Select the best answers to the following questions based on a close and thorough reading of "Roanoke, the Lost Colony."

1. What is most likely the author's purpose for describing the second expedition?

   A. to provide background information about the Roanoke colony

   B. to suggest that John White was an extremely poor governor

   C. to imply that the third expedition was doomed from the start

   D. to explain how John White's map was created

   E. to show the evolution of the Roanoke colony

2. Which of the following could be omitted to strengthen Paragraph 5?

   A. "What occurred in Roanoke while White was away?"

   B. "It is also possible the Anglo-Spanish War spilled over to Roanoke…"

   C. "Yet, no remains were found, and there were no signs of violence…"

   D. "…only to be lost at sea?"

   E. "It wouldn't be unlikely."

3. In the paragraph that begins, "Croatoan—now called Hatteras Island," what does the author mean when she says, "It may seem unbelievable"?

   A. English artifacts were found on Croatoan.

   B. Despite what happened previously, the natives helped the colonists.

   C. It is impossible to pity the English settlers at Roanoke.

   D. A writing tablet was found, even though the colonists were illiterate.

   E. The gold ring that was found belonged to the Kendall family.

117

4. What is the most likely reason the second site is called "Site X"?

   A. Nobody knows the Native American name of the site.

   B. Researchers want to distinguish it from Croatoan.

   C. John White referred to it as Site X in his journal.

   D. The island is shaped like an X.

   E. It is named after the mark on John White's map.

5. Which of the following is NOT mentioned in the passage?

   A. Border ware was found at Site X.

   B. Croatoan was what is modern-day Hatteras Island.

   C. Civilians were brought to Roanoke on the third expedition.

   D. Archaeologists found part of a rapier at Croatoan.

   E. John White wanted to stay in England to fight in the war.

EXERCISE 4 / MAKING INFERENCES

Choose the best answer.

1. Which of the following locations is the most likely to be **devoid** of people?

   A. an enormous mansion

   B. an old bookstore

   C. a vacant lot

   D. a quiet library

2. Which of the following would be considered a **precarious** situation?

   A. enjoying a sunny day

   B. winning the lottery

   C. lighting a campfire

   D. getting lost in the woods

3. If a boy is described as **contentious**, he would most likely respond to a rude comment by
   A. respectfully explaining that the comment is offensive.
   B. ignoring the comment and walking away.
   C. insulting the speaker and picking a fight.
   D. making a sarcastic comment and laughing.

4. An organization **cognizant** of the fact that a person is a spy would probably NOT
   A. give her secret information.
   B. capture and question her.
   C. give her false information.
   D. reveal her true identity.

5. Based on the passage, it can be inferred that the Spanish Armada is
   A. the name of the Spanish army.
   B. a fleet of Spanish ships.
   C. a disease unique to Spain.
   D. the name of the Spanish queen.

EXERCISE 5 / ROOTS, PREFIXES, AND SUFFIXES

Answer the questions below that are designed to help you arrive at some conclusions about word families and origins.

1. Briefly define **amicable** in your own words. What part of speech is **amicable**?

   _____

   _____

   A. Divide **amicable** into its two probable word elements (not syllables).

   _____

   _____

   B. You should be familiar with the second of these elements. What does it mean?

   _____

   _____

C. Consider the first element, the root, and this list of words that contain the same root. Define each in your own words. Feel free to look up any words you do not know, but make certain you do not merely copy the definition verbatim from your source.

amiable:

_____

_____

amigo:

_____

_____

amity:

_____

_____

What does the root of **amicable** mean based on the meanings of the words above?

_____

_____

D. Briefly explain in your own words how **amicable** derives its meaning from is parts.

_____

_____

2. Briefly define **cognizant** in your own words. What part of speech is **cognizant**?

_____

A. Divide **cognizant** into its two probable word elements (not syllables).

_____

B. Which of the word's three elements establishes its part of speech? List other familiar words that contain this same element and define each in your own words. Feel free to look up any words you do not know, but make certain you do not merely copy the definition verbatim from your source.

_____

_____

_____

_____

_____

What does this word element most likely mean?

_____

_____

C. Now consider this list of related words. Define each in your own words. Feel free to look up any words you do not know, but make certain you do not merely copy the definition verbatim from your source.

recognize:

_____

_____

precognition:

_____

_____

incognito:

_____

_____

cognitive:

_____

_____

What apparent root do all of these words share? What does this root most likely mean?

_____

_____

_____

_____

D. Even without examining the one remaining element, you should be able to explain in your own words how **cognizant** derives its meaning from is parts.

_____

_____

_____

_____

CREATURES OF THE ABYSS

Imagine you are all alone in your floating steel-clad capsule, shrouded in complete darkness, where the sun is almost a hundred million miles away. The environment is more hostile than any you've ever experienced before. If you go outside, you will die from the immense pressure, lack of oxygen, and extreme temperature. A malfunction of your capsule could lead to your death.

Remarkably, life forms move around you, making you a bit curious about how they can withstand the pressure. Their appearances are both fascinating and **disquieting**. Some have glowing lights suspended from their foreheads, as well as rows of razor-sharp teeth. Others have protruding snouts, in addition to jaws that launch forward to snap their prey in two, or eyes that can move on the top of their heads to see the surface above them. Even the cutest of the bunch, a creature with floppy, ear-like extensions, can devour animals twice its size, completely whole.

Where *are* you? Some planet in another solar system?

Believe it or not, you are on Earth. You are in the Marianas Trench, the deepest place on the planet.

The Marianas Trench
Northwest of Guam, in the Pacific Ocean, is the Marianas Trench. The Challenger Deep, the lowest part of the trench, extends 6.8 miles below the surface of the water, making it the lowest location on Earth. The **prodigious** amount of pressure in this area of never-ending darkness is roughly 8 tons per square inch, almost 1,100 times greater than it is at sea level. The temperature of the water ranges from 34-39°F, but is close to 572°F near volcanic vents that spew hot chemicals from the earth's molten core into the boiling water.

How, you might wonder, could creatures live there?

Surprisingly, many do, and they have developed unique adaptations to help them thrive in their environment.

Anglerfish
The anglerfish may look like a monster from your nightmares, but it is, in fact, one of the greatest marvels in the animal world. There are more than 200 species, ranging in color from reddish-brown to black, and they live at various depths between 2,600 and 3,200 ft. Their numerous sharp fangs, protruding jaws, and crescent-shaped mouths set them apart from other fish, but what is most unique about anglerfish, however, is the light suspended over their head. The appendage is actually how the fish got its name: The odd growth looks like a fishing rod with a lure attached. In fact, it actually *is* a lure, and it is used to attract prey and potential mates. The technical name for the lure is the *esca*. Anglerfish also produce bioluminescence—the way their bodies glow—in the same way that fireflies do. Bacteria living within the esca get protection and **sustenance** from the fish and, in exchange, give the lure its characteristic glow. The fish's unique adaptations make it an adroit hunter, enabling it to take advantage of the darkness.

Barreleye Fish
The barreleye fish gets its name from its tubular-shaped eyes—a characteristic that, by itself, may not seem particularly interesting. What makes the fish unique and fascinating, though, is that it can move its eyes 90°, from the usual forward-looking position to one that peers directly upward. It can then look directly through its *transparent head*. Since there is only a small glimmer of light 2,500 ft. below the surface, the fish has to use whatever is available to detect its prey, usually seeing

silhouettes in conditions nearly **bereft** of light. Its eyes are contained in a fluid shield used for protection. The fluid shield holding the eyes also serves another purpose by protecting it from stings of creatures it hunts, such as jellyfish. Although the fish looks odd, it obviously has successfully adapted to its environment.

Goblin Shark

The goblin shark is another creature that may be terrifying in appearance, but is actually an evolutionary wonder. Its features allow it to survive between 900 and 4,000 ft. deep in extreme pressure and near darkness. The goblin shark can catch prey that is significantly faster than it is. The shark varies in length from 10-13 ft. long, and it moves rather slowly. Still, two of its adaptations help it overcome that **detriment**.

The goblin shark has a long, protruding snout, the *rostrum*, which is full of sensors that detect electrical currents created by the movement of living creatures. Furthermore, the shark has developed another fascinating feature: unique jaws that **contort** and rapidly extend the teeth past the shark's body, allowing it to grab and eat its prey. At these depths, in the dark water with very little available food, every advantage must be used in order to become an **efficacious** predator.

Dumbo Octopus

The dumbo octopus dwells between 9,800 and 13,000 ft. below the surface of the water and is only 8-12 in. long. It has eight webbed tentacles and semi-**translucent** skin that gives only a hazy view of its body, but its most outstanding features are the two fins resembling ears that extend from its head. Its name, not surprisingly, alludes to the large-eared elephant from the Disney movie. While the octopus may seem cute, its appearance is deceiving. The dumbo octopus is a **voracious** predator capable of eating prey much larger than itself, bypassing chewing and devouring it whole.

Many other strange, seemingly otherworldly creatures live in the vast expanse of the pitch-black ocean. We continue to gaze in wonder at the sky, dreaming of the distant worlds waiting to be explored. But shouldn't we think about looking down instead? There are still mysteries on our own planet, including the **enigmas** of the Marianas Trench.

EXERCISE 1 / WORD LIST

Use the context in which the word is used to determine what the word probably means. Write a brief definition in the space provided.

1. **bereft:** _____

   Since there is only a small glimmer of light 2,500 ft. below the surface, the fish has to use whatever is available to detect its prey, usually seeing silhouettes in conditions nearly **bereft** of light.

2. **contort:** _____

   Furthermore, the shark has developed another fascinating feature: unique jaws that **contort** and rapidly extend the teeth past the shark's body, allowing it to grab and eat its prey.

3. **detriment:** _____

   The shark varies in length from 10-13 ft. long, and it moves rather slowly. Still, two of its adaptations help it overcome that **detriment**.

4. **disquieting:** _____

   Their appearances are both fascinating and **disquieting**. Some have glowing lights suspended from their foreheads, as well as rows of razor-sharp teeth. Others have protruding snouts, in addition to jaws that launch forward to snap their prey in two, or eyes that can move on the top of their heads to see the surface above them.

5. **efficacious:** _____

   At these depths, in the dark water with very little available food, every advantage must be used in order to become an **efficacious** predator.

6. **enigma:** _____

   There are still mysteries on our own planet, including the **enigmas** of the Marianas Trench.

7. **prodigious:** _____

   The **prodigious** amount of pressure in this area of never-ending darkness is roughly 8 tons per square inch, almost 1,100 times greater than it is at sea level.

8. **sustenance:** _____

   Bacteria living within the esca get protection and **sustenance** from the fish and, in exchange, give the lure its characteristic glow.

9. **translucent:** _____

It has eight webbed tentacles and semi-**translucent** skin that gives only a hazy view of its body, but its most outstanding features are the two fins resembling ears that extend from its head.

10. **voracious:** _____

The dumbo octopus is a **voracious** predator capable of eating prey much larger than itself, bypassing chewing and devouring it whole.

EXERCISE 2 / USING WORDS IN CONTEXT

Fill in the blank with the vocabulary word that best completes the sentence. In some cases, you may need to change the tense or form of a verb or the number of a noun.

detriment	voracious	enigma	sustenance	bereft
efficacious	translucent	disquieting	prodigious	contort

1. The movement on the other side of the door was _____, and Isabelle was afraid that there was a ghost in her bedroom.

2. This excellent bug-repelling candle is _____ in keeping mosquitos away from your campsite.

3. The ancient, secret society remained a(n) _____ since little evidence could be found about its strange rituals.

4. Christina's face _____ into a look of disgust when she saw the trash her roommate left in the living room.

5. The Sunday flea market contains a(n) _____ number of antiques from over thirty vendors.

6. Cows require only grass for their _____, so many small farmers never give them grain for food.

7. The winds—not the temperature—proved to be the biggest _____ for early explorers of the Antarctic.

8. The lamp had a(n) _____ shade that gave the room a soft glow.

9. A belief that the earth is flat may seem _____ of reason in today's world.

10. The dog had such a(n) _____ appetite that she ate her treat without chewing it.

EXERCISE 3 / READING COMPREHENSION AND ANALYSIS

Select the best answers to the following questions based on a close and thorough reading of "Creatures of the Abyss."

1. The purpose of the first four paragraphs of the passage is to
   A. introduce the species that will be discussed.
   B. emphasize the otherworldliness of the Marianas Trench.
   C. allow the reader to visualize the unfamiliar environment.
   D. caution future astronauts to be careful in space.
   E. evoke a feeling of unease in the reader.

2. The passage is primarily organized by
   A. location.
   B. order of importance.
   C. chronology.
   D. point and counterpoint.
   E. order of dangerousness.

3. How could the "Barreleye Fish" section of the passage be improved?
   A. add a concluding sentence
   B. elaborate on how the fish sees silhouettes
   C. omit the information about the "tubular-shaped eyes"
   D. mention the depth at which the creature lives
   E. remove one of the two sentences about the fluid shield

4. Which of the following is a logical contradiction to a statement the author makes?
   A. Goblin sharks also live off the coast of Africa and Australia.
   B. The animals are difficult to study because they can't live outside their natural habitats.
   C. "Barreleye Fish" is actually a term used to describe multiple species.
   D. Dumbo octopus feed on the plants at the bottom of the trench.
   E. The electro-sensors on the goblin shark's rostrum are called the "ampullae of Lorenzoni."

5. Which is NOT a fact mentioned in the passage?

    A. Dumbo octopus live between 9,800 and 13,000 ft. below the water's surface.

    B. Female anglerfish are significantly larger than male anglerfish.

    C. The temperature of the water near the vents is over 500°F.

    D. Much of the Marianas Trench has yet to be explored.

    E. Goblin sharks have a special adaptation to overcome their slow speed.

EXERCISE 4 / MAKING INFERENCES

Choose the best answer.

1. Someone who encounters an **enigma** would most likely

    A. imitate it.

    B. replace it.

    C. study it.

    D. disregard it.

2. A **voracious** reader would most likely

    A. have a library card.

    B. leave her favorite book at school.

    C. use excellent grammar.

    D. know a lot of stories.

3. You would most likely find **disquieting** situations in which genre of movies?

    A. romance

    B. suspense

    C. drama

    D. comedy

4. Which of the following is the best example of the word **prodigious**?

   A. The harbor was surrounded by prodigious rock formations that were higher than the tallest ships.

   B. The prodigious expert on zoology did not recognize the animal that washed up on the shore.

   C. Both species of fish were actually prodigious and native to the area.

   D. Telling Maria that she was again "Employee of the Month" took a prodigious effort from her manager.

5. Which of the following can be correctly inferred from the section about goblin sharks?

   A. Animals need to be fast in order to be good predators.

   B. Goblin sharks' jaws launch forward at a great speed.

   C. Goblin sharks are the only species of shark that has a rostrum.

   D. No other shark species live in the Marianas Trench.

EXERCISE 5 / ROOTS, PREFIXES, AND SUFFIXES

Answer the questions below that are designed to help you arrive at some conclusions about word families and origins.

1. Briefly define **prodigious** in your own words. What part of speech is **prodigious**?

   _____

   _____

   A. Divide the word into its three elements.

      _____

      _____

   B. Which element identifies the word's part of speech? What sense or meaning does this particular element give the word? List some other words that use this suffix.

      _____

      _____

      _____

      _____

C. List some other words that share the same prefix as **prodigious**. Define each in your own words. What does this prefix most likely mean?

_____

_____

_____

_____

_____

D. Briefly explain in your own words how **prodigious** derives its meaning from its parts.

_____

_____

_____

_____

2. Briefly define **translucent** in your own words. What part of speech is **translucent**?

_____

_____

_____

_____

A. Divide the word into its three probable word elements.

_____

_____

_____

B. You are probably already familiar with the third of these elements. List some other words that contain this suffix and define each in your own words. What function does this suffix perform and what does it mean?

_____

_____

_____

_____

_____

_____

C. You are also probably already familiar with the first of these elements. List some other words that contain this prefix and define each in your own words. What function does this prefix serve?

_____

_____

_____

_____

_____

D. Given the meaning of the word **translucent** and the meanings of the word's prefix and suffix, what can you infer the root means? What does the word **translucent** *literally* mean?

_____

_____

_____

_____

_____

THE SPEED OF LIGHT

- The highest speed ever achieved in a land vehicle is 763 miles per hour.
- The speed of sound is 767 mph.
- A rifle bullet travels about 1,700 mph.
- The fastest a jet plane ever flew is 2,193 mph.
- A rocket must go 25,000 mph to escape Earth's gravity.
- The earth itself travels around the sun at about 67,000 mph.

All these numbers, though, are completely insignificant when **juxtaposed** with the speed of light. Light travels 186,000 miles, not an hour, but a *second*!

The speed of light is so unfathomably great that it is difficult for humans to conceive of. After all, the instant you turn on a lamp, illumination appears. The distance from the light bulb to even the farthest wall is relatively short, and it doesn't take long for the light particles to reach it.

Light from the sun takes over eight minutes to reach Earth, but what if the distance were considerably greater—say, between the earth and Proxima Centauri, the closest star beyond our solar system? Light from that star **traverses** twenty-five *trillion* miles of space to reach us, and light travels about six trillion miles in one year. Therefore, light from Proxima Centauri takes over four years to get to Earth. The effects of this tremendous speed and the time it takes light to travel enormous distances—even at such a high speed—are fascinating and surprising.

In a way, telescopes are like "time machines," looking into the past. Telescopes, whether they use light, radio, or infrared waves, receive an image of that distant star as it appeared 4.2 years ago. (Remember, that's how long it took its light to reach Earth.) **Subsequently**, astronomers 4.2 years in the future will see Proxima Centauri as it is today.

Unlike anything else we know of, the speed of light cannot be exceeded. It is what scientists call a "constant" because it never deviates from 186,000 miles per second. Since the speed of light is **invariable** and unchanging, as is the distance it travels in a year, physicists have created a unit of measurement, a *light year*, to conveniently explain how far apart different celestial bodies are.

The speed of light is an **integral** concept in physics. Scientists and the public alike have shown great **deference** to the genius of Albert Einstein, who created the most well-known scientific equation ever, $E = mc^2$. He used the speed of light to **delineate** the connection between mass and energy. While some people might think that only physicists can understand the **esoteric** equation, the explanation is fairly straightforward: E means *energy*, m is the *mass* of something, and c^2 stands for the *speed of light squared*. It's easy to see that the energy in even the tiniest things is enormous, which is why nuclear reactions produce huge amounts of energy. It also explains why nuclear weapons are so devastating. If we could release all the energy contained within the atoms of something even as small as a pin, there would be enough energy to cause an immensely powerful explosion.

It may sound strange, but there is an unexpected link between light speed and the passage of time. The faster one moves toward the speed of light, the slower time passes—in other words, if you began traveling through space quickly enough, you could theoretically get a few extra minutes to your day! The idea may seem odd, especially because we move so slowly that we wouldn't discern a change in time; unless you've been to space, you have never traveled faster than 2,193 mph.

One person who has experienced this slower passage of time, often called "time dilation," is astronaut Scott Kelly. Kelly spent a year aboard the International Space Station (ISS), orbiting the earth at approximately 17,500 mph. He has an identical twin, Mark. Because of the time Scott spent in the ISS, he aged slightly slower than Mark, who remained on Earth. It sounds incredible, but Scott Kelly is now 13 milliseconds younger than he would have been if he had never been in space. That 17,500 mph orbital speed is an **infinitesimal** percentage of the speed of light, so a person traveling close to 186,000 miles per second would lose substantially more time. Reaching the speed of light, however, is an impossibility because mass is an impediment. Objects with mass cannot meet the speed of light, while light—which has no mass—can!

The speed of light, by itself, is fascinating, especially since no human-created craft has even come close to it. Discovering more about light has led scientists to challenge other concepts that we once thought were consistent, including the passage of time. Modern-day physicists carry on Einstein's research and continue to learn more about light, **elucidating** its connection to mass, energy, and time.

EXERCISE 1 / WORD LIST

Use the context in which the word is used to determine what the word probably means. Write a brief definition in the space provided.

1. **deference:** _____

   Scientists and the public alike have shown great **deference** to the genius of Albert Einstein, who created the most well-known scientific equation ever, $E = mc^2$.

2. **delineate:** _____

   [Einstein]…used the speed of light to **delineate** the connection between mass and energy.…*E* means *energy*, *m* is the *mass* of something, and c^2 stands for the *speed of light squared.*

3. **elucidate:** _____

   Modern-day physicists carry on Einstein's research and continue to learn more about light, **elucidating** its connection to mass, energy, and time.

4. **esoteric:** _____

   While some people might think that only physicists can understand the **esoteric** equation, the explanation is fairly straightforward…

5. **infinitesimal:** _____

   That 17,500 mph orbital speed is an **infinitesimal** percentage of the speed of light, so a person traveling close to 186,000 miles per second would lose substantially more time.

6. **integral:** _____

   The speed of light is an **integral** concept in physics. Scientists and the public alike have shown great deference to the genius of Albert Einstein, who created the most well-known scientific equation ever, $E = mc^2$. He used the speed of light to delineate the connection between mass and energy.

7. **invariable:** _____

   It is what scientists call a "constant" because it never deviates from 186,000 miles per second. Since the speed of light is **invariable** and unchanging, as is the distance it travels in a year…

8. **juxtapose:** _____

   All these numbers, though, are completely insignificant when **juxtaposed** with the speed of light. Light travels 186,000 miles, not an hour, but a *second*!

9. **subsequent:** _____

In a way, telescopes are like "time machines," looking into the past. Telescopes, whether they use light, radio, or infrared waves, receive an image of that distant star as it appeared 4.2 years ago. (Remember, that's how long it took its light to reach Earth.) **Subsequently**, astronomers 4.2 years in the future will see Proxima Centauri as it is today.

10. **traverse:** _____

Light from that star **traverses** twenty-five *trillion* miles of space to reach us, and light travels about six trillion miles in one year.

EXERCISE 2 / USING WORDS IN CONTEXT

Fill in the blank with the vocabulary word that best completes the sentence. In some cases, you may need to change the tense or form of a verb or the number of a noun.

esoteric	invariable	delineate	elucidate	infinitesimal
juxtapose	integral	deference	traverse	subsequent

1. A clean layout and exciting graphics are _____ in creating a good webpage.

2. Darlene's arrival time seemed _____; she always showed up at exactly 10 a.m., but last Wednesday, she didn't appear until 10:30.

3. The Maltese may seem like a small dog until it's _____ against the tiny Chihuahua.

4. The historian _____ the globe looking to record hundreds of local urban legends.

5. Maria forgot to turn off the faucet and, _____, flooded the entire bathroom.

6. The television host _____ how the bones found on Nikumaroro Island were declared to be Amelia Earhart's.

7. The dusty old books contained _____ information that would make sense only to cultures that worshipped the sun.

8. John White _____ the coasts of Virginia and North Carolina on his map for fellow explorers to follow.

9. Maria dyed her hair green and yellow for Prom, but in _____ to her mom's objections, went back to her original color the next day.

10. Considering he just learned to play chess, there is only a(n) _____ chance that Shane will win the game tonight.

EXERCISE 3 / READING COMPREHENSION AND ANALYSIS

Select the best answers to the following questions based on a close and thorough reading of "The Speed of Light."

1. The purpose of this passage is to

    A. entertain.

    B. persuade.

    C. inform.

    D. express a viewpoint.

    E. refute an argument.

2. How can the paragraph beginning, "Light from the sun…" be improved?

    A. create a better transition between it and the next paragraph

    B. write "twenty-five trillion" as a number

    C. describe the appearance of Proxima Centauri

    D. explain that light doesn't have mass

    E. omit the sentence about Proxima Centauri's light reaching Earth

3. Based on what you have read in the passage, why will astronomers 4.2 years from now see Proxima Centauri as it is today?

    A. The International Space Station will begin orbiting the star.

    B. Proxima Centauri will be 4.2 light years closer to Earth.

    C. Future astronomers will have better telescopes to view the star.

    D. Great distances prevent the progression of time in outer space.

    E. Light from the star today will reach Earth in 4.2 years.

4. In the paragraph that begins, "It may sound strange," why does the author use the specific speed "2,193 mph."

    A. It is almost three times the speed of sound.

    B. The speed is the fastest a jet plane has ever traveled.

    C. Scott Kelly traveled much faster when the ISS orbited Earth.

    D. It is much slower than the speed of light.

    E. It is an exaggeration of how fast humans can travel.

5. What is time dilation?

   A. the amount of time gained when traveling in a space station

   B. the inability to surpass the speed of light

   C. the increase of speeds expressed in the miles-per-hour list

   D. the slowing of time as speed increases

   E. the length of time it takes light from a celestial body to reach Earth

EXERCISE 4 / MAKING INFERENCES

Choose the best answer.

1. Which of the following shows a **subsequent** action?

   A. a student giving a presentation

   B. two instruments playing together

   C. a runner winning a race

   D. results of a bad decision

2. Which is the best example of two things **juxtaposed** against each other?

   A. people holding hands

   B. different versions of a story

   C. a car in a parking garage

   D. two countries sharing a border

3. If David wanted to **elucidate** a complex idea about coding, he would probably NOT

   A. explain it using an analogy.

   B. draw it as a diagram.

   C. use complicated language.

   D. describe it multiple ways.

4. Of the following, which could be described as **infinitesimal**?

   A. a dust particle

   B. the size of the universe

   C. the Atlantic Ocean

   D. a collection of quarters

5. Why does the author say telescopes "are like 'time machines' "?

    A. They can view objects several light years away.

    B. They illustrate the evolution of technology.

    C. They can see light that left celestial objects in the past.

    D. They are evidence that ancient people were astronomers.

EXERCISE 5 / ROOTS, PREFIXES, AND SUFFIXES

Answer the questions below that are designed to help you arrive at some conclusions about word families and origins.

1. Define **elucidate** in your own words. What part of speech is **elucidate**?

    _____

    A. Divide the word into its three most likely elements or components.

    _____

    B. List some other words that most likely contain the same prefix. Define each in your own words.

    _____

    _____

    _____

    _____

    _____

    C. What does this prefix most likely mean?

    _____

    D. In Chapter 14, you encountered the word **translucent**, which shares a common root with **elucidate**. What is this common root and what does it mean?

    _____

    E. Briefly explain in your own words what **elucidate** literally means and how it might derive its current usage from this literal meaning

    _____

    _____

    _____

2. Define **integral** in your own words. What part of speech is **integral**?

_____

A. Divide the word into its three most likely elements or components (not syllables).

_____

B. Consider this list of related words. Define each in your own words. Feel free to look up any words you do not know, but make certain you do not merely copy the definition verbatim from your source.

integrate:

_____

_____

integer:

_____

_____

integrity:

_____

_____

C. What apparent root do these words share? What does this root most likely mean?

_____

_____

D. You should already be familiar with the word's prefix. What is it, and what does it mean?

_____

_____

E. Consider this list of words that contain the same suffix as **integral**. What function does the suffix perform in all of these words?

annual, conditional, individual, procedural, textual

_____

_____

_____

F. Briefly explain in your own words how **integral** derives its meaning from its parts.

_____

_____

_____

STONE AGE SURGERY

If you were an archaeologist digging at a prehistoric burial site and you uncovered a skull with an enormous hole through it, initially, it may seem to **evince** terrible violence and a tragic death. Maybe the person was a prisoner from another tribe who was **interrogated** and tortured. Maybe he was a criminal executed for some type of crime. Maybe he was a warrior who received the horrific injury in battle.

You could imagine any number of similar scenarios. Unfortunately, you'd always reach an incorrect conclusion. That hole was actually made for a medical or ritual purpose, likely with the person's consent. Furthermore, he or she probably survived.

The strange procedure is known as "trepanation."

Trepanation is an operation that has existed since ancient times. A hole was created in the front or side of the skull (rarely in the back) by drilling, cutting, or scraping. While the task was sometimes performed with **rudimentary** objects like seashells, there were also special tools, called trepans and raspatories, created for the purpose. Trepans sawed or drilled the cranium, and raspatories scraped it. In the process, which took place while the patient was *conscious*, no damage was done to the underlying blood vessels or brain. The hole remained open, eventually to be covered by the skin. The operation was done on people of all ages, social statuses, and stages of health, as well as both genders.

The technique was not restricted to a particular region or specific time period. It was, instead, used everywhere from Middle America to Asia. Based on archaeological findings, it is clear that trepanation was used at least as far back as 5000 BCE. Later, Ancient Greek and Roman civilizations adopted the method. Around 400 BCE, Hippocrates, "The Father of Western Medicine," wrote about trepanation in his **treatise**, *On Injuries of the Head*. He used the procedure to cure people of various brain injuries. Specifically, he used the procedure to remove blood from the cranium. He understood that stagnant blood will eventually clot and cause permanent damage or death. The same kind of operation was later used by Galen (129–c. 210 AD), a Roman surgeon. He believed that trepanation removed pressure following traumatic head injuries. The practice continued into the Middle Ages and was even portrayed in paintings from that era. One of the most famous is *The Extraction of the Stone of Madness* by the Dutch artist Hieronymus Bosch.

Since the surgeries were dangerous and **excruciating**, what induced doctors to perform them? There are several hypotheses. More than one could be true, based on the time period and part of the world. Trepanation could have been done for health reasons, for instance, to relieve patients of epilepsy, migraines, ulcers, or hemorrhages. Because remains have been found of individuals with no **overt** signs of illness, it is also possible that trepanations were done for religious or spiritual reasons. Ancient doctors may have mistaken epilepsy and mental illness for demonic possession and thought drilling holes in the skull would allow the evil to leave the affected person's body.

Although trepanation may initially appear to be an archaic and absurd surgery, it is actually done today, but, of course, with anesthesia. The operation, however, goes by two other names: "craniotomy" and "craniectomy." In craniotomies, part of the skull is removed over the affected area of the brain and then repositioned at the end of the operation. The procedure is used to remove tumors, cysts, or blood clots, take samples of brain tissue for biopsy, and analyze parts of the brain using a tiny, lighted microscope with a camera. In craniectomies, however, a piece of skull is removed and stored in a freezer until the patient has healed. This method is used primarily to remove pressure in the cranium after severe brain trauma. Once the swelling has **dissipated**, the piece of skull can be replaced.

As strange as it sounds, even with the **advent** of modern science, some people have attempted to perform trepanation on *themselves*. One of the most famous incidents involves Bart Huges, a New Age doctor with dubious medical views, unproven by scientific studies. He believed that creativity was associated with the amount of blood flowing to the brain. According to Huges, humans began to lose blood volume when they learned to walk upright. This change supposedly caused an increase in cerebrospinal fluid (CSF). CSF is a colorless liquid in the brain and spinal cord. Huges believed that the greater the ratio of blood to CSF, the more creativity a person had. He theorized that creating a hole in the skull would increase (not decrease) the pressure in the cranium. This would

cause some CSF to drain away, allowing the person to become more artistic. Since no doctor would perform the surgery, Huges operated on himself with a dentist's drill in 1965. Although he claimed that he achieved the desired effects, the scientific community found no proof that the procedure improved brain functionality. Huges wrote about his experience in his autobiography, *The Book with the Hole*. He also continued advocating trepanation. He lived an additional 39 years and died from an unrelated cause.

With the elimination of ancient superstitions, it is easy to **discredit** these types of unusual treatments, especially those supposedly removing supernatural entities from an individual's body or increasing his or her creativity. However, there are actually some benefits to trepanation. Although Hippocrates and Galen did not know what scientists know today, they were correct in their belief that cutting a hole in someone's skull could **alleviate** pressure in the cranium and help treat abnormalities in the brain. While trepanation may initially seem like a ludicrous, outdated technique, the ancient practice was more useful than previously thought.

EXERCISE 1 / WORD LIST

Use the context in which the word is used to determine what the word probably means. Write a brief definition in the space provided.

1. **advent:** _____

   As strange as it sounds, even with the **advent** of modern science, some people have attempted to perform trepanation on *themselves*.

2. **alleviate:** _____

   Although Hippocrates and Galen did not know what scientists know today, they were correct in their belief that cutting a hole in someone's skull could **alleviate** pressure in the cranium and help treat abnormalities in the brain.

3. **discredit:** _____

   With the elimination of ancient superstitions, it is easy to **discredit** these types of unusual treatments, especially those supposedly removing supernatural entities from an individual's body or increasing his or her creativity.

4. **dissipate:** _____

   This method is used primarily to remove pressure in the cranium after severe brain trauma. Once the swelling has **dissipated**, the piece of skull can be replaced.

5. **evince:** _____

   If you were an archaeologist digging at a prehistoric burial site and you uncovered a skull with an enormous hole through it, initially, it may seem to **evince** terrible violence and a tragic death.

6. **excruciating:** _____

   Since the surgeries were dangerous and **excruciating**, what induced doctors to perform them?

7. **interrogate:** _____

   Maybe the person was a prisoner from another tribe who was **interrogated** and tortured.

8. **overt:** _____

   Because remains have been found of individuals with no **overt** signs of illness, it is also possible that trepanations were done for religious or spiritual reasons.

9. **rudimentary:** _____

   While the task was sometimes performed with **rudimentary** objects like seashells, there were also special tools, called trepans and raspatories, created for the purpose.

10. **treatise:** _____

    Around 400 BCE, Hippocrates, "The Father of Western Medicine," wrote about trepanation in his **treatise**, *On Injuries of the Head.*

EXERCISE 2 / USING WORDS IN CONTEXT

Fill in the blank with the vocabulary word that best completes the sentence. In some cases, you may need to change the tense or form of a verb or the number of a noun.

discredit	overt	alleviate	treatise	excruciating
dissipate	advent	interrogate	evince	rudimentary

1. The pain in Kelly's arm was so _____ that she had to be taken to the hospital.

2. When she discovered the broken television, Mrs. Mitchell _____ her children to find out who had done it.

3. Joseph took an aspirin to _____ his terrible headache.

4. The large amounts of volcanic rock _____ that there had been an eruption recently.

5. The two experts on UFO encounters were _____ when it was discovered their videos were faked.

6. John Locke's *Two _____ of Government* contained ideas that greatly inspired the American Revolution.

7. Although there were no _____ signs, the way Jessie was acting suggested something bad had happened.

8. Even though there were some earlier films made, the 1900s marked the real _____ of motion pictures.

9. The concept of velocity is a(n) _____ idea in physics on which many theories are based.

10. The fog on the mountain began to _____ when the sun finally rose.

EXERCISE 3 / READING COMPREHENSION AND ANALYSIS

Select the best answers to the following questions based on a close and thorough reading of "Stone Age Surgery."

1. Why is the title unsuitable for the passage?

    A. Only a portion of the passage discusses trepanation during the Stone Age.

    B. The title is uninteresting and does not capture the reader's interest.

    C. Readers won't know the time period in which the Stone Age occurred.

    D. The title should focus on trepanation in modern medicine.

    E. Trepanation is not considered a form of surgery.

2. Which sentence in Paragraph 4 could be omitted without detracting from the message?

    A. "Trepanation is an operation that has existed since ancient times."

    B. "A hole was created in the front or side of the skull (rarely in the back) by drilling, cutting, or scraping."

    C. "While the task was sometimes performed with rudimentary objects like seashells, there were also special tools, called trepans and raspatories, created for the purpose."

    D. "The hole remained open, eventually to be covered by the skin."

    E. "The operation was done on people of all ages, social statuses, and stages of health, as well as both genders."

3. How is this passage organized?

    A. topic

    B. location

    C. point and counterpoint

    D. order of importance

    E. chronology

4. Re-read the following sentence:

   "Although Hippocrates and Galen did not know what scientists know today, they were correct in their belief that cutting a hole in someone's skull could alleviate pressure in the cranium and help treat abnormalities in the brain."

   Which is NOT one of the brain abnormalities that trepanation can help treat?

   A. mental illness

   B. tumors

   C. cysts

   D. brain trauma

   E. blood clots

5. The introduction serves to

   A. connect a modern medical practice to an ancient technique.

   B. suggest that the Stone Age was a dangerous time period.

   C. show how archaeology can be an exciting field of study.

   D. emphasize the oddity of trepanation by juxtaposing violence with healing.

   E. demonstrate how we can draw incorrect conclusions by misinterpreting evidence.

EXERCISE 4 / MAKING INFERENCES

Choose the best answer.

1. Something in a **rudimentary** stage could include

   A. a movie that is earning a lot of money.

   B. a book that is losing popularity.

   C. a screenplay that is being written.

   D. a song that is number one on the charts.

2. In order to **alleviate** stress, one would probably NOT

   A. go for a walk.

   B. meditate.

   C. talk to a friend.

   D. work even harder.

3. Which of the following is NOT something that could **dissipate**?

   A. fear

   B. confusion

   C. smoke

   D. seeds

4. Which of the following would be an **overt** sign that two people don't like each other?

   A. They give each other angry looks.

   B. They make sarcastic remarks to each other.

   C. They insult each other.

   D. They ignore one another.

5. Re-read the following excerpt from the passage:

   "One of the most famous incidents involves Bart Huges, a New Age doctor with dubious medical views, unproven by scientific studies."

   Based on the context, New Age most likely means

   A. based on original ideas.

   B. advanced and modern.

   C. anticipating the future.

   D. outside of the mainstream.

EXERCISE 5 / ROOTS, PREFIXES, AND SUFFIXES

Answer the questions below that are designed to help you arrive at some conclusions about word families and origins.

1. Define **advent** in your own words. What part of speech is **advent**?

   _____

   A. Divide the word into its two most likely elements or components.

   _____

B. Look at this list of words derived from the same root as **advent**. Each word has been divided into its primary elements or components, many of which should already be familiar to you. Define each in your own words and explain how it derives its meaning from its parts.

venue (venue):

_____

avenue (a + venue):

_____

convene (con + vene):

_____

convention (con + ven + tion):

_____

circumvent (circum + vent):

_____

intervene (inter + vene):

_____

C. Consider the meaning of the word **advent** and the other words above, what does their common root, *vene*, most likely mean?

_____

D. Consider the following words, which all begin with the same prefix as **advent**. Each has been divided into its primary elements or components, many of which should already be familiar to you. Briefly define each in your own words. Feel free to consult a dictionary or other source that explains word history in its definitions, but do not merely copy the information verbatim from the source.

adapt (ad + apt):

_____

adhere (ad + here):

_____

adjacent (ad + jacent):

_____

adopt (ad + opt):

_____

advocate (ad + voc + ate):

_____

What meaning do all of these words have in common? What does their shared prefix most likely mean?

_____

_____

_____

2. Define **discredit** in your own words. What part of speech is **discredit**?

   _____

   A. Divide the word into its two most likely elements or components.

      _____

   B. List some other words that most likely contain the same prefix as **discredit**. Define each in your own words. What does their common prefix mean?

      _____

      _____

      _____

      _____

      _____

      _____

      _____

   C. In Chapter 3, "Aliens at Roswell?" you encountered the words **credence** and **incredulous**, which share a common root with **discredit**. What is this common root, and what does it mean?

      _____

   D. Briefly explain in your own words how **discredit** derives its meaning from its parts.

      _____

      _____

      _____

BIGFOOT

An unknown creature tramps through the imaginations of many people, leaving behind distinctive footprints—human-like, but gigantic. The beast, which resembles a primate, is a biped of imposing size, between 7 to 8 feet in height, with a muscular frame and a weight estimated at approximately 650 lbs. It is covered from head to toe in red to dark-brown hair, and the deep-set eyes on its face are hidden beneath a protruding brow. Surely, encountering such a being would be unnerving, causing you to stop and gape at the curious figure or, perhaps more likely, run away in fear. Fortunately, the creature wouldn't pursue you. You'd escape unharmed.

Bigfoot certainly is a phenomenon, but not the one you might think. The fact that the belief in its existence is sustained, despite all major, supposedly **empirical** evidence having been exposed as *fake*, is fascinating.

Why do people believe in Bigfoot as **adamantly** as they do?

It can't be denied that the creature *is* a prominent figure in Native American folklore. "Sasquatch," another one of Bigfoot's names, is derived from "Sésquac," a term meaning "wild man" in the language of the Coastal Salish tribes of Washington State and British Columbia. Other tribes have given the **entity** different names. In the Native American community, while there is some debate over whether it is an actual mammal or a supernatural being, it is treated with great respect. The Sasquatch, to them, is both a guardian and a warning. In some ways, it is a **harbinger** of doom, signifying trouble in the community that will evolve into chaos if changes aren't made.

But even if Bigfoot has a history in ancient legend, why should that give credence to its existence? Why Bigfoot and not wendigos, pukwudgies, and deer women? The answer is that several events occurred that brought the creature into the media spotlight and made it a part of mainstream culture. Even though every instance has been revealed as a hoax, it has not stopped many people from affirming that an elusive being still roams the wilderness of the Pacific Northwest.

One of the first times Bigfoot entered the news was in 1958. Gerald Crew, a construction worker, was doing roadwork in Weitchpec, California, when he came across an enormous set of human-like footprints. He used plaster to make castings of the prints, and *The Humboldt Times* reported the story of the finding in its October 5th issue. The creature was given the name "Bigfoot," the same **epithet** used by people at the nearby logging sites to describe it. The footprint was convincing and seemed to be certain proof of Bigfoot's existence. It deceived people until 2002, when it was discovered to have been a prank carried out by a man named Ray Wallace using a pair of carved wooden feet.

The second major time Bigfoot walked onto the scene was in 1967. Roger Patterson and Bob Gimlin, two former rodeo riders, had heard stories about a mysterious entity wandering in California's Six Rivers National Forest. The men went to investigate on horseback, and when they reached the area of Bluff Creek, they caught a glimpse of a figure and filmed a clip of the enormous hominid passing through the shot. The footage would become one of the most scrutinized videos in history, and to Sasquatch believers, it was definitive proof of the creature's existence. However, like the 1958 footprints, the video was a fraud. Evidently, one of Patterson's friends, Bob Heironimus, was promised $1,000 to put on an ape suit and walk through the area. Yet, despite his convincing performance, he was never paid. Patterson died in 1972, but Gimlin has become famous. While those who understand that the film is a fake have responded with **censure** and ridicule, Bigfoot aficionados, despite it all, admire Gimlin, viewing him as a Bigfoot expert.

An additional, comical hoax occurred more recently, in 2008. Two hikers, Matt Whitton and Rick Dyer "found" a Sasquatch body frozen in a block of ice in the mountains of northern Georgia. The body appeared to be about 7 ft. 7 in. tall and weigh 500 lbs. The men sold it to the researchers at Squatchdetective, a website and radio show dedicated to the investigation of Bigfoot. Needless to say, believers all over the world were **exhilarated** to finally have proof that it exists! Steve Hulls, the director and host of Squatchdetective, and his team began the thawing process and immediately noticed that something was amiss. The hair on the creature's body melted when burned, and parts of the head looked unusually hollow. Most importantly, the characteristic feet appeared to have been made of rubber. It wasn't Bigfoot. It was simply an empty gorilla costume.

Despite the overwhelming evidence suggesting Bigfoot is nothing more than a hoax, there are still those who **tenaciously** cling to the idea that this creature exists and continue the search. One such person is Dr. Jeffrey Meldrum, a professor of anatomy and anthropology at Idaho State University and author of the 2006 book *Sasquatch: Legend Meets Science*. In 2012, he began **collaborating** on a project with another believer, who claimed to have seen Bigfoot in the forests of northern California back in 1997. The two actively sought fiscal support to pay for the building of a remote-controlled blimp with thermal-imaging software. The blimp would fly over the forests to, they hoped, get images of the creature—this time maybe, against all odds, finally proving that it exists.

Shockingly, the Bigfoot myth is **perpetuated** despite there being no proof that the creature exists. Not only is there a lack of existing reliable data, but all new information is either **inconclusive** or false. All the hoaxes, which should be deleterious to the myth of Sasquatch's existence, seem to be ignored by those who firmly believe in the creature. The true mystery of Bigfoot is not what it actually is, but rather, how so many people can be deceived into believing such a ludicrous idea.

EXERCISE 1 / WORD LIST

Use the context in which the word is used to determine what the word probably means. Write a brief definition in the space provided.

1. **adamant:** _____

   The fact that the belief in its existence is sustained, despite all major, supposedly empirical evidence having been exposed as *fake*, is fascinating. Why do people believe in Bigfoot as **adamantly** as they do?

2. **censure:** _____

   While those who understand that the film is a fake have responded with **censure** and ridicule, Bigfoot aficionados, despite it all, admire Gimlin, viewing him as a Bigfoot expert.

3. **collaborate:** _____

   In 2012, he began **collaborating** on a project with another believer, who claimed to have seen Bigfoot in the forests of northern California back in 1997.

4. **empirical:** _____

   The fact that the belief in its existence is sustained, despite all major, supposedly **empirical** evidence having been exposed as *fake*, is fascinating.

5. **entity:** _____

   Other tribes have given the **entity** different names. In the Native American community, while there is some debate over whether it is an actual mammal or a supernatural being, it is treated with great respect.

6. **epithet:** _____

   The creature was given the name "Bigfoot," the same **epithet** used by people at the nearby logging sites to describe it.

7. **exhilarated:** _____

   Needless to say, believers all over the world were **exhilarated** to finally have proof that it exists!

8. **harbinger:** _____

   The Sasquatch, to them, is both a guardian and a warning. In some ways, it is a **harbinger** of doom, signifying trouble in the community that will evolve into chaos if changes aren't made.

9. **inconclusive:** _____

   Not only is there a lack of existing reliable data, but all new information is either **inconclusive** or false.

10. **perpetuate:** _____

    Shockingly, the Bigfoot myth is **perpetuated** despite there being no proof that the creature exists.

11. **tenacious:** _____

    Despite the overwhelming evidence suggesting Bigfoot is nothing more than a hoax, there are still those who **tenaciously** cling to the idea this creature exists and continue the search.

EXERCISE 2 / USING WORDS IN CONTEXT

Fill in the blank with the vocabulary word that best completes the sentence. In some cases, you may need to change the tense or form of a verb or the number of a noun.

epithet	perpetuate	harbinger	inconclusive	collaborate	entity
tenacious	censure	empirical	adamant	exhilarated	

1. Richard I, the English king, earned the _____ "the Lionheart" because of his bravery in battle.

2. The politician was subjected to serious _____ by her colleagues, as well as the public when she made insensitive comments about the disaster victims.

3. The thunder in the distance served as the _____ of an oncoming storm.

4. The results of the tests were _____, and the doctors couldn't determine the cause of Rob's symptoms.

5. Phil's numerous absences and frequent tardiness _____ the idea that he was lazy and unmotivated.

6. The philosophies of David Hume were based on _____ observations, rather than theories.

7. Despite all the setbacks in his life, Chris _____ held on to the idea that he would be successful someday.

8. Our two laboratories had to _____ on the study, sharing information, resources, and personnel.

9. We were _____ when we heard that three of our favorite bands would be playing at the venue down the street.

10. Emily was _____ that the game was rigged since nobody could find the last clue to the puzzle.

11. The psychic claimed that she was communicating with a supernatural _____.

EXERCISE 3 / READING COMPREHENSION AND ANALYSIS

Select the best answers to the following questions based on a close and thorough reading of "Bigfoot."

1. In this passage, the author's main intent is to
   A. present facts about Bigfoot hoaxes.
   B. describe Native American beliefs.
   C. entertain the reader.
   D. detail the complicated hunts for Bigfoot.
   E. express an opinion.

2. Which of the following is the best paraphrase of the quotation?

   "All the hoaxes, which should be deleterious to the myth of Sasquatch's existence, seem to be ignored by those who firmly believe in the creature."

   A. All the Sasquatch hoaxes should be ignored because the creature is real.
   B. The hoaxes should harm belief in Sasquatch, but they don't.
   C. Believers in Sasquatch are harmed by ignoring the hoaxes.
   D. The existence of Sasquatch hoaxes makes supporters more firm in their beliefs.
   E. The myth of Sasquatch believers is a deleterious hoax that should not be believed.

3. What does the author think is the true Bigfoot phenomena?
   A. People continue to believe in Bigfoot without evidence.
   B. Bigfoot can survive the harsh environments of the Pacific Northwest.
   C. Bigfoot and humans evolved from the same species.
   D. A creature Bigfoot's size had gone undetected for so long.
   E. Bigfoot-like creatures are always spotted alone.

155

4. What, if true, could negatively affect the author's reasoning that the Gimlin film is fake?

   A. Patterson and Gimlin weren't former rodeo riders.

   B. The video wasn't filmed at Bluff Creek.

   C. Heironimus lied about being in the film.

   D. Heironimus did get paid to participate.

   E. Roger Patterson knew Ray Wallace.

5. Which of the following does NOT accurately represent a comment the author makes about what happened in 1967?

   A. Patterson and Gimlin achieved a great deal of fame due to the film.

   B. Bigfoot actually was a man who was wearing an ape suit.

   C. Heironimus did not receive money for participating.

   D. Gimlin's part in the hoax actually led to his fame.

   E. The video has been examined many times.

EXERCISE 4 / MAKING INFERENCES

Choose the best answer.

1. A person who is **adamant** that she is correct would probably NOT

   A. share her opinion with others.

   B. listen to another viewpoint and change her mind.

   C. consider only evidence that supports her opinion.

   D. point out how someone else's objections are wrong.

2. One thing that someone trying to **perpetuate** the ideas of a famous scholar would probably do is

   A. argue in a blog that the scholar is wrong.

   B. read more of that scholar's writings.

   C. compare the ideas to those of other scholars.

   D. agree with criticisms of the scholar.

3. An example of people **collaborating** could include

    A. two friends sitting next to each other in a cafeteria.

    B. filmmakers criticizing each other's works.

    C. students completing a group assignment.

    D. two employees working on separate reports.

4. Which of the following is NOT an example of a person being **tenacious**?

    A. a detective checking every single lead on a case

    B. an athlete exercising for three hours every morning

    C. a student up late at night studying for a test

    D. a man who is constantly changing jobs

5. Re-read the following sentence from the passage:

    "But even if Bigfoot has a history in ancient legend, why should that give credence to its existence? Why Bigfoot and not wendigos, pukwudgies, and deer women?"

    Based on the context, it can be inferred that "wendigos, pukwudgies, and deer women" are

    A. other creatures from Native American folklore.

    B. other names for Bigfoot.

    C. creatures that resemble Bigfoot.

    D. creatures that live in the Pacific Northwest.

EXERCISE 5 / ROOTS, PREFIXES, AND SUFFIXES

Answer the questions below that are designed to help you arrive at some conclusions about word families and origins.

1. Define **collaborate** in your own words. What part of speech is **collaborate**?

    _____

    A. Divide the word into its three most likely elements or components.

    _____

    B. You are probably already familiar with the first and third of these elements. What do they mean?

    _____

    _____

C. Consider the following verbs, which all begin with the same root as **collaborate**. Each has been divided into its primary elements or components, some of which are probably already familiar to you. Briefly define each in your own words. Feel free to consult a dictionary or other source that explains word history in its definitions, but do not merely copy the information verbatim from the source.

labor (labor):

_____

belabor (be + labor):

_____

elaborate (e + labor + ate):

_____

What meaning do all of these words have in common? What does their shared root most likely mean?

_____

_____

_____

D. Put the elements together and briefly explain how **collaborate** derives its meaning from its parts.

_____

2. Define **inconclusive** in your own words. What part of speech is **inconclusive**?

_____

A. Divide the word into its four most likely elements or components.

_____

B. You are probably already familiar with the first and second of these elements. What do they mean?

_____

_____

C. Consider the following words, all of which are derived from the same root as **inconclusive**. Each has been divided into its primary elements or components, many of which should already be familiar to you. Briefly define each in your own words. Feel free to consult a dictionary or other source that explains word history in its definitions, but do not merely copy the information verbatim from the source.

conclude (con + clude):

_____

include (in + clude):

_____

inclusive (in + clus + ive):

_____

exclude (ex + clude):

_____

exclusive (ex + clus + ive):

_____

close (close):

_____

enclose (en + close):

_____

What meaning do all of these words have in common? What does their shared root most likely mean?

_____

_____

_____

D. List some other words that end with the same suffix as **inconclusive**. Define each in your own words. What function does their common suffix perform? What does it mean?

_____

_____

_____

_____

_____

_____

_____

E. Put the elements together and briefly explain what **inconclusive** literally means and how it derives its meaning from its parts.

_____

_____

_____

_____

_____

VOCABULARY

adamant	*adj.*	insistent, firm, stubborn
adroit	*adj.*	skillful; clever
advent	*noun*	the arrival or coming into existence of
aesthetic	*noun*	pertaining to beauty
affinity	*noun*	an attraction to
affluent	*adj.*	wealthy
aficionado	*noun*	a person who understands and deeply appreciates a subject or thing
aftermath	*noun*	the results of
align	*verb*	to position along a line; to give support to
allege	*verb*	to state or present without substantial evidence
alleviate	*verb*	to relieve or make easier to endure
altercation	*noun*	a heated argument
amicable	*adj.*	friendly
anomaly	*noun*	a deviation from the norm; an odd or peculiar occurrence
archaic	*adj.*	referring to something that is outdated or no longer used
arduous	*adj.*	difficult to accomplish
ascertain	*verb*	to determine with certainty
ascribe	*verb*	to credit or attribute to
assimilate	*verb*	to adopt the culture of another group of people
attest	*verb*	to declare as true
audacity	*noun*	boldness, usually in defiance of some rule
awry	*adv.*	departing from the expected course
bereft	*adj.*	lacking; deprived

celestial	*adj.*	pertaining to the sky or the heavens
censure	*noun*	severe criticism
circumnavigate	*verb*	to travel or circle completely around something, often in reference to the earth
cogent	*adj.*	convincing; sound
cognizant	*adj.*	aware or having knowledge of
collaborate	*verb*	to work together on a project
colloquial	*adj.*	informal and everyday, generally applying to speech
concentric	*adj.*	placed within one another so as to have a common center
concurrent	*adj.*	occurring at approximately the same time
conjecture	*noun*	a conclusion drawn with little evidence
constitute	*verb*	to make up from smaller parts
contentious	*adj.*	argumentative
contort	*verb*	to bend or twist out of shape
conundrum	*noun*	a puzzle; a difficult or confusing problem
convoluted	*adj.*	complicated; difficult to understand
copious	*adj.*	large in amount or quantity
corroborate	*verb*	to add evidence to; to make certain
credence	*noun*	a belief in the accuracy or truth of something
credible	*adj.*	believable; reasonable
decimate	*verb*	to destroy completely
deference	*noun*	submissive respect
deleterious	*adj.*	having a harmful effect; causing injury
delineate	*verb*	to describe; to depict
demeanor	*noun*	one's attitude or mannerisms

denizen	*noun*	a citizen; an inhabitant
denote	*verb*	to indicate
depiction	*noun*	a description or representation
deplete	*verb*	to completely reduce the amount of
deride	*verb*	to insult; to criticize
detriment	*noun*	a disadvantage
deviate	*verb*	to move away from or not do what is expected
devoid	*adj.*	not possessing something that should be present
differentiate	*verb*	to separate and determine the differences
diffuse	*verb*	to freely move and spread; to scatter
diminutive	*adj.*	small in size
discern	*verb*	to distinguish differences; to detect
discourse	*noun*	a discussion
discredit	*verb*	to disprove; to show to be untruthful
disproportionate	*adj.*	too large or small in comparison with something else
disquieting	*adj.*	disturbing; alarming
dissimilar	*adj.*	different from; not alike
dissipate	*verb*	to gradually disappear or lessen
dubious	*adj.*	unreliable; doubtful; questionable
edifice	*noun*	a large building or structure
efficacious	*adj.*	effective
elicit	*verb*	to draw forth or bring about
elucidate	*verb*	to explain; to make clear
emanate	*verb*	to come forth; to send forth
eminent	*adj.*	prominent; important; outstanding

empirical	*adj.*	based on proof rather than theory
enigma	*noun*	a mystery; something difficult to understand
entity	*noun*	something that exists; a being
epithet	*noun*	a name given based on a characteristic
erroneous	*adj.*	false, incorrect
esoteric	*adj.*	understood by only a small group of people with specialized knowledge
evince	*verb*	to show evidence of; to make clear
evoke	*verb*	to bring to mind
excruciating	*adj.*	extremely painful
exhilarated	*adj.*	overjoyed
expound	*verb*	to put forward an idea; to explain; to state
extant	*adj.*	existing
fabricate	*verb*	to invent or create, sometimes to deceive
facilitate	*verb*	to make easier
factious	*adj.*	causing disagreement
fissure	*noun*	an opening; a groove; a split
forensic	*adj.*	used for court or legal reasons, usually referring to science
fortuitous	*adj.*	lucky; by chance
guile	*noun*	cunning; deceit; cleverness
gullible	*adj.*	easily fooled or tricked
harbinger	*noun*	a sign or an omen
hypothesis	*noun*	an idea put forth to explain something
immutable	*adj.*	unchangeable, fixed
impediment	*noun*	a barrier; an obstruction
impervious	*adj.*	unable to be affected by; resistant to

impropriety	*noun*	inappropriateness
incomprehensible	*adj.*	unable to be understood
inconclusive	*adj.*	doubtful or questionable; without a specific conclusion
incongruous	*adj.*	incompatible; not harmonious
incredulous	*adj.*	unwilling to believe that something is true; skeptical
indeterminate	*adj.*	uncertain; indefinite
indicative	*adj.*	showing or revealing something
inexplicable	*adj.*	unable to be explained
infinitesimal	*adj.*	very small; so tiny as to be barely measureable
innate	*adj.*	existing in one's nature rather than being learned
insatiable	*adj.*	unable to be satisfied
inscrutable	*adj.*	unable to be understood; mysterious
insuperable	*adj.*	unable to be overcome
insurmountable	*adj.*	unable to be conquered or overcome
integral	*adj.*	being an essential part of
interaction	*noun*	the way that things affect each other
interrogate	*verb*	to question for information, often in a formal matter
intrinsic	*adj.*	of or relating to something's basic nature
invaluable	*adj.*	significant; important
invariable	*adj.*	unchanging, constant
inveterate	*adj.*	habitual; continuing
irrefutable	*adj.*	unable to be disproved; undeniable
iteration	*noun*	a version of something
juxtapose	*verb*	to place next to for comparison or contrast
labyrinthine	*adj.*	consisting of a complicated network or involved process

ludicrous	*adj.*	ridiculous
lustrous	*adj.*	shining; glowing
maniacal	*adj.*	suggesting madness or insanity
meticulous	*adj.*	paying careful attention to detail
minuscule	*adj.*	very small
mitigate	*verb*	to lessen the severity of
myriad	*adj.*	great in number
omnipotence	*noun*	the state of having absolute power
opulence	*noun*	luxury; wealth
orient	*verb*	to adjust relative to a specific position
overt	*adj.*	clearly demonstrated or displayed
pandemic	*noun*	a general, widespread outbreak, usually of a disease
paragon	*noun*	the perfect example of
pathogenic	*adj.*	causing or capable of causing disease
patriarchal	*adj.*	relating to a society or family ruled by men
perpetuate	*verb*	to cause to continue; to preserve indefinitely
physiological	*adj.*	relating to chemical and biological functions within an organism
plethora	*noun*	an abundance; an excess
polytheism	*noun*	a belief in many gods
populace	*noun*	the population of people; the public
postulate	*verb*	to claim to be true
precarious	*adj.*	dangerous; uncertain
preposterous	*adj.*	absurd and illogical
prestigious	*adj.*	well regarded; exceptional
prodigious	*adj.*	extraordinary in size or amount; very impressive

prolific	*adj.*	producing something in abundance
pseudonym	*noun*	a pen name; an alias
purported	*adj.*	appearing or claimed to be true
recipient	*noun*	one who receives something
reconnaissance	*noun*	a preliminary act to gather information
refute	*verb*	to disprove
relegate	*verb*	to assign, usually to an inferior class or role
rudimentary	*adj.*	at an early stage of development; basic
ruse	*noun*	a trick
salient	*adj.*	significant; important
satiate	*verb*	to fill completely; to satisfy
serendipitous	*adj.*	happening fortunately and by accident
spurious	*adj.*	false, incorrect
subsequent	*adj.*	occurring after something else
substantiate	*verb*	to support with evidence
substantive	*adj.*	considerable; clear, meaningful, and, therefore, important
surreptitious	*adj.*	secret or stealthy
susceptible	*adj.*	capable of being exposed to some action or effect
sustenance	*noun*	nourishment
tectonic	*adj.*	relating to faults in the earth's crust
tenacious	*adj.*	firmly holding on to; determined
translucent	*adj.*	allowing some light to pass through; almost transparent
traverse	*verb*	to move across or along
treatise	*noun*	an in-depth written discussion on a subject
ubiquitous	*adj.*	present everywhere at once

unequivocal	*adj.*	clear; leaving no doubt
usurp	*verb*	to seize a position, title, or authority with no right to do so
venerate	*verb*	to respect, worship, or revere
veracity	*noun*	truthfulness; accuracy
veritable	*adj.*	real or genuine
vibrant	*adj.*	bright; appearing full of life and energy
voracious	*adj.*	extremely hungry; very eager